What teens are saying about the
Taste Berries™ *for Teens Journal*

"I was one of the teens who worked on this journal so I got a chance to go through it along the way. I love it—and the process of journaling—because as I wrote down my thoughts to some very straight-on questions, I found myself face-to-face with some parts of me that I didn't know as well as I thought I did. I was surprised that my heart knew things I hadn't put into words before. By the time I had completed the journal, I felt as though I had a new friend. Journaling really is that powerful—especially with this journal. It helps you think about a lot of things, and sort out some of the major stuff teens go through—from breakups to makeups, from easing up on stress to figuring out what to do after high school."

—Jenna McCarthey, 16

"When I read *Taste Berries for Teens* it got me thinking about a lot of things. This journal is perfect for helping me take a closer look at all those issues—like getting along with my friends and even my teachers—and how to not be so stressed out."

—Cory Johnson, 14

"This journal makes you think. It has lots of fun questions about your friends, your relationships, even about how to make your dreams come true. The part I liked the most was thinking through what my life would look like in five years—from the kind of car I would be driving to the apartment I would have, to what kinds of new friends I would choose. I found that exercise so important because it got me thinking about why I need to do well in school. Now I understand what I want, and I'm ready to do what it takes to reach my goals."

—Calle Tiller, 16

"I had a blank journal once, but I never seemed to know what to write in it—so I didn't write anything. This journal is great because it asked me the questions that I wanted to write the answers to!"

—Ryan Moehn, 15

"This journal practically saved my life! I had no idea what I was going to do after I graduated. I didn't know whether I wanted to go to college or what kind of a career I wanted. There were just a lot of big changes going on, and I admit, I was scared. This journal took me by the hand and helped me figure it all out, so now I know what direction I'm headed in and what my goals are for the future."

—Jamie Kristophersen, 17

"This journal makes it fun and easy to write about the things that matter most, like your friends, your family and your feelings."

—Heather Hall, 13

"This journal is so cool. Not only do I understand myself better now, it's like I've written a book about myself—*My Life as a Teen.*"

—Lauren Anthony, 18

"My first year of high school I was totally preoccupied with fitting in with all my friends. After writing about this in my journal, I'm more concerned with making sure my life works."

—Stephanie Stam, 15

"I've kept a diary for three years, so when my dad gave me this journal as a gift 'just because,' I was excited to try it out because it's different from the others I have. I love this journal because it's not just recording my life as it is. I really hadn't ever thought about being able to create the life I want—I was mostly going along with the flow—but this journal inspires me to create a me I can live up to."

—**Shelly Moreno, 16**

"Journaling is awesome because I get to express my feelings and thoughts. I'm finding that I keep changing—even reading what I wrote just a month ago, I can see how my feelings have changed about things. It's nice to look over what I've written, and to see that I've grown."

—**Brittany Meredith, 15**

"At first I thought, 'A diary! No way! Guys don't keep a diary!' But this isn't a diary. It's a journal—a guide to help you understand what you want and how to go about getting it. This has been a process, a good one. For sure it's changed my attitude about how much control I have over my life—and my future!"

—**Guy Baker, 17**

"Shortly after I bought this journal for my fifteen-year-old daughter, she asked, 'Mom, what do you think my personality traits are?' Puzzled, I asked why she wanted to know and was pleasantly surprised to learn she was asking for a section in her journal on discovering what she wanted to do in life. As I answered her question, we had a great conversation. Since she's been using her journal, not only is she better able to identify what's important to her, we're also getting to know each other better."

—**Peggy McDermott, mother**

Taste Berries™
for Teens
JOURNAL

My Thoughts on Life, Love and Making a Difference

With contributions from teens for teens

Bettie B. Youngs, Ph.D. &
Jennifer Leigh Youngs

authors of *Taste Berries for Teens: Inspirational Short Stories and Encouragement on Life, Love, Friendship and Tough Issue*

SCHOLASTIC INC.
New York   Toronto   London   Auckland   Sydney
Mexico City   New Delhi   Hong Kong

We would like to acknowledge the following publishers and individuals for permission to reprint the following material. (Note: The stories that were penned anonymously, that are public domain or were previously unpublished stories written by Bettie B. Youngs or Jennifer Leigh Youngs are not included in this listing. Also not included in this listing but credited within the text are those stories contributed or based upon comments by teens.)

The Paintbrush, by Lee Ezell, adapted from *You and Self-Esteem: A Book for Young People.* ©1996 Bettie B. Youngs. Reprinted with permission.

Did I Pass Your Test for Friends?, by Elmer Adrian. Reprinted with permission.

I Have to Live with Myself and So . . . , excerpted from *I CAN Ignite the Community Spirit: 301 Ways to Turn Caring into Action*, by Joy J. Golliver and Ruth Hayes-Arista. ©1997 Joy J. Golliver and Ruth Hayes-Arista. Reprinted with permission.

Kevin Got "Lucky", by Bettie B. Youngs. Reprinted with permission by publisher Health Communications, Inc., Deerfield Beach, Florida, from *Gifts of the Heart* by Bettie B. Youngs. ©1996 Bettie B. Youngs, Ph.D., Ed.D. Adapted from the story "Just Lucky."

ISBN 0-439-25615-1

12 11 10 9 8 7 6 5 4 3 2 1   0 1 2 3 4 5/0

Printed in the U.S.A.   23

First Scholastic printing, October 2000

Cover illustration and design by Andrea Perrine Brower
Inside book design by Lawna Patterson Oldfield

With love we dedicate this book to
the many teens whom we have worked with
over the past several years.
We share their concerns and hopes
for a life of love, friendship and purpose.
Our hope is for your inspiration—
that you might become all that is
in your hearts and souls.

Contents

Acknowledgments

Jennifer and I would like to thank some of the "taste berries" in the development of this journal—it was a far greater challenge than we had first imagined. To all the teens who so diligently worked with us on the *Taste Berries for Teens* book and then again on this journal, a bushel of taste berries to you! Your friendship is near and dear to our hearts. In some cases we feel like we've been big sisters to you, but mostly, we feel like you've been loving teachers to us. As always, to our publisher, Peter Vegso, and the staff at Health Communications— a very special thanks. Christine Belleris, Matthew Diener, Lisa Drucker, Allison Janse, Erica Orloff—your encouragement, support and professional assistance is just the *best!* And thanks to all the many others at HCI who work magic in global ways, giving wings to their mission of making a difference one life at a time—or as they say, "changing the world one book at a time." To Andrea Perrine Brower, for the way she works taste-berry magic with shape and color to flavor the covers and pages of this and many of our other books. Her work is, as teens say, "hot!" A very special taste-berry thanks to Tina Moreno from our staff. We shudder to think what we would do without her; she keeps us in the right place at the right time, and in the designated city and on the right date! We also thank Carrie Hague, our student intern on this project, and the countless other young people who read and had input into the assembly of this journal.

And to some very delicious and important taste berries in our lives: First to Arlene Burres, mother and grandmother, who at this writing is ill. This glorious woman is a pillar of strength to both of us, and our hearts are heavy with concern for her—and bottomless with love as well. We also thank the loyal and loving support of father and grandfather Everett Burres, "Good Guys" Dic Youngs and David Kirk, and best friend Tawny Pearl Flippen. Never do we take your love and friendship for granted. And as always, we give glory to God, from whom all blessings flow.

Introduction

Dear Reader,

When we wrote *Taste Berries for Teens: Inspirational Short Stories and Encouragement on Life, Love, Friendship and Tough Issues,* we hoped that you would be inspired by the stories from other teens who are doing awesome things in their schools and communities—giving and sharing their time and talents to make a difference in the lives of others. So, we were most happy to learn that reading of their efforts prompted you to get involved in activities of your own to make the world— and the lives with whom you share it—a better place to live. We had also hoped that those stories from teens who spoke candidly about how they cope with the ups and downs of life would help you consider how to best cope with your own. Once again, your letters assured us this, too, was happening. We are pleased to assist you in your search for being your personal best, and honored to add you to our growing list of friends.

In writing *Taste Berries for Teens,* we worked with young adults of all ages and backgrounds from across the country. We got to know so many teens. After the book's release, we heard from so many more as your letters began pouring in.

We hear you. Your joys, your struggles, the hope, the pain—all imprint your dreams and aspirations for the direction you want your life to take.

Committed to helping you continue your search for being the best you can be, we decided to create a tool to help you do that—the *Taste Berries for Teens Journal!* Whether writing about matters that are confusing to you or about those things that make you happy and light up your life, journaling is a powerful way to look deep within your own heart and clarify choices that are best and right for you. From being a friend to ending a friendship; from doing what it takes to go to college to deciding what sort of a job and career you'd like; from coping with a tough issue to not getting all stressed out over it, journaling can help you see what's really on your mind and then make decisions and set goals to help you get what you want out of life.

This journal is divided into seven parts, each one designed to help you examine specific topics you told us are important to you. Because each unit stands alone, it's okay to do them in whatever order you'd like. To begin, find the topic that you're most interested in and then let the questions guide you in exploring it in depth. Take your time. Some questions will be easy to answer, while others may take a great deal of intro-spection. Some even require that you seek the input of others—feedback that you won't want to miss!

After filling in your journal, go back and read what you've written. This will help you understand yourself even better than you already do, and help you make decisions about what you would like to do—and need to do. It can also help you see how much you are growing and changing during this time in your life. As importantly, going back over your journal from time to time can help you acknowledge the taste berry in you—the ways you make your life, and the lives of others, better.

What is a taste berry? A taste berry is a glorious little fruit that mysteriously convinces the taste buds that all food—even food that is distasteful—is delicious. The bright little berry (artfully shown on the cover of this book in psychedelic colors!) has been used by aboriginal tribes around the world for countless years to make the sometimes necessary eating of bitter roots—and grubs— tolerable. People can be—and need to be—"taste berries" to each other. When we help others—such as by being a considerate and trusted friend—we sweeten life's joys and ease the bitterness of its disappointments and losses.

Just think what a wonderful place the world will be when we each do our part by being a taste berry! Consider this journal your very own guide—your personal voice and trusted companion—to knowing and honoring your ability to make a difference in your own life and that of others.

As always, we would love to hear from you. We are currently working on *More Taste Berries for Teens,* a second book of inspirational stories on things that are real issues for teens and the ways they are creatively coping with their lives and making a difference in the lives of others. So if you have stories you'd like to submit for consideration, please send them to us at:

More Taste Berries for Teens
c/o Tina Moreno
3060 Racetrack View Drive #101
Del Mar, CA 92014

"Taste Berries" to you!

PART 1

Who I Am: Creating an Identity of My Own

*Our life is like a
piece of paper on which every
passerby leaves a mark.*

—Chinese Proverb

I Am . . . Accept Me as I Am . . . Who Am I? . . .

The Paintbrush

I keep my paintbrush with me, wherever I may go,
In case I need to cover up, so the real me doesn't show.
I'm so afraid to show you me; afraid of what you'll do,
I'm afraid you'll laugh or say mean things; afraid I might lose you.

I'd like to remove all the layers, to show you the real, true me,
But I want you to try to understand; I need you to like what you see.
So if you'll be patient and close your eyes, I'll remove the coats real slow,
Please understand how much it hurts, to let the real me show.

Now that my coats are all stripped off, I feel naked, bare and cold,
And if you still find me pleasing, you are my friend, pure as gold.
I need to save my paintbrush though, and hold it in my hand,
I need to keep it handy in case someone doesn't understand.

So please protect me, my dear friend, and thanks for loving me true,
And please let me keep my paintbrush with me, until I
love me, too.

—Lee Ezell, *Taste Berries for Teens*

What is your paintbrush—how do you "cover up" when you need to?

_____

_____

_____

_____

_____

_____

_____

_____

_____

_____

_____

Every artist dips his brush into
his own soul, and paints his own nature
into his picture—as he does
in living his life.

—HENRY WARD BEECHER

Taste-Berry Decisions:
An Identity of Your Own

Do you ever "play into" or portray an image you believe someone else holds of you even though it's "not you"? For example, do you wear your hair in a certain style (or color) or dress or behave in a certain way because you think someone else will like you better if you do? Describe a time when you "covered up" who you are in order to gain someone's acceptance or approval. What did you do? *What* were you covering up? What "image" were you trying to present? Whose acceptance or approval were you trying to win?

_____

_____

_____

_____

Did it work—was that person impressed? Did he or she like you better as a result of the image you presented? Did you "fool" that person into thinking you were who you represented? How do you know? How did you feel about the whole thing? If you fooled someone, how did this make you feel about that person?

_____

_____

_____

_____

Why did you feel you had to act in a way other than your authentic self?

_____

_____

_____

_____

_____

_____

_____

_____

_____

_____

_____

_____

The journey of a thousand miles starts
from beneath your feet.

—*Tao Te Ching*

What Do You Think About Me?
Do You Accept Me as I Am?

It's only natural to want to be liked and accepted by others. Though we may not always ask aloud, we are always wondering:

"Do you think I'm okay?"
"Do you like the way I look?"
"Do you approve of how I act?"
"Do you like me?"
"Do you accept me as I am?"
"Do you like the way I dress?"
"Will you stick by me in good times and bad?"
"Will you be my friend—always?"

What else would you add to this list?

♡ _____

♡ _____

♡ _____

♡ _____

♡ _____

♡ _____

♡ _____

♡ _____

♡ _____

We want the answer to each of these questions to be an enthusiastic "Yes!" When others like us and accept us, we feel valued—like we're a terrific person. And that's a good feeling.

Who, more than anyone else, makes you feel like a "terrific" person?

_____

_____

_____

_____

Knowing others is intelligence; knowing yourself is true wisdom.

—*Tao Te Ching*

What does that person do to make you feel so good about yourself, so special? For example: Does he or she support you in being your best? Is he or she patient with you? Does he or she give you the benefit of the doubt? Does he or she trust you? Is he or she a good listener, one who always pays close attention to what you say? Does he or she respect your opinion even if it is different than his or her own? Can you count on this person to be on your side when your values are put to the test—such as being pressured to smoke, drink, do drugs or have sex? Is this person kind to you, sensitive to your feelings and gentle with your heart?

List six things that person says or does that make you feel like a terrific person.

♡ _____

_____

♡ _____

_____

♡ _____

_____

♡ _____

_____

♡ _____

_____

♡ _____

_____

How does this "positive review" contribute to the image you hold of yourself?

_____

_____

_____

_____

Who counts on you to see him or her as being special?

_____

_____

_____

_____

What three things do you do that create a positive picture for
that person?

1 _____

_____

2 _____

_____

3 _____

_____

When soul rises to lips you feel
the kiss you've wanted.

—RUMI

Who I Am . . . Accept Me as I Am . . .

Even though we may want to feel accepted by others, it doesn't always work out that way. Sometimes this doesn't bother us, but most of the time, especially if their approval is important to us, we feel rejected, hurt or left out. It's only natural to feel this way.

Write about a time when you really wanted a certain person to think well of you and it just didn't happen. Who was the person? How long had you been hoping to gain this person's friendship before you realized there wasn't much of a chance? Why didn't he or she "like" you? How do you know if this was really the case? How did not gaining this person's friendship or acceptance make you feel about yourself? How did it make you feel about the other person?

_____

_____

_____

_____

_____

Do you think it's important to always work toward getting others to like us? How important is it to you?

_____

_____

_____

_____

When someone doesn't like you as much as you would like them to, how does it change the way you feel about yourself?

_____

_____

_____

_____

What do you do when someone doesn't like you as much as you would like? For example, do you write that person a letter telling him or her about your feelings? Or do you go on about your business, reminding yourself that you have other friends and focusing on being a good friend to them—and to yourself? Do you withdraw, feel sad or cry? How long does it take you to get over feeling rejected?

_____

_____

_____

_____

_____

If a friend asked you for advice on what he or she should do if having a difficult time gaining the friendship or acceptance of someone, what would you tell your friend?

_____

_____

_____

_____

What Are You Most Afraid Others Will Not Like About You?

So many things about being a teen-ager are tough. One of them is being told to "be yourself," when the other part of that message—even though it's silent—is "as long as you're beautiful, cheerful and thin." Everyone wants you to be perfect in every way. I know a lot of kids who "cover up" because it's so impossible to be like we're supposed to be. I've had a lot of trouble being perfect. When I look in the mirror, I don't see "perfect." Trying to be perfect while knowing I wasn't made it even worse. I got depressed. Depression is a terrible thing. I felt like I was in a deep, black hole and couldn't get out. So I tried to be extra pleasant and funny so that no one would know how depressed I was, but after a while I wasn't able to pretend anymore. Then my friends gave me a hard time because I was always feeling down. Nobody wants to hear that you're "feeling down." It's funny how that works, but it's true. It got to a point where I wondered if maybe I was crazy or something. But now I've been diagnosed with Bipolar Disorder so I'm on medications to help my body do what it's supposed to do. Now that I know what's causing me to feel this way, I no longer have to paint myself to be someone I'm not. What a relief.

—Alana Ballen, 14, *Taste Berries for Teens*

What do you try to cover up about yourself? What are you most afraid that others will not like about you? Why do you think they won't like that part of you?

_____

_____

_____

_____

_____

_____

_____

_____

_____

_____

_____

_____

_____

_____

*If only we could stop
trying to be happy we could have
a pretty good time.*

—EDITH WHARTON

Who Am I? . . . I Am . . .

*Sometimes I am meeting a part of
myself for the first time.*
—JENNIFER LEIGH YOUNGS, *TASTE BERRIES FOR TEENS*

What do you think Jennifer's quote means?

_____

_____

_____

_____

Everyone is always saying, "Be yourself," but who is your "true self" anyway? Are you shy or outspoken? Fun-loving or laid back? Are you sporty, artsy, spiritual, intellectual? Write down words or phrases that best describe you.
I am:

_____

_____

_____

*Nothing will take the place of a shelf full
of books by one's own chair.*
—EDWARD NEWTON

Who Do You Think I Am?

Do your friends see you as you see yourself? Ask a good friend to describe you. (If you don't feel comfortable having your friend write in your journal, ask him or her to write on a sheet of paper.)

My name is _____ and I would describe

_____ as a person who is _____

_____

_____

Now ask your mom to describe you. (If you don't feel comfortable having your mother write in your journal, ask her to write on a sheet of paper.)

I am _____'s mother, and I would describe

_____ as a person who is: _____

_____

_____

Now ask your dad to describe you. (If you don't feel comfortable having your father write in your journal, ask him to write on a sheet of paper.)

I am _____'s dad, and I would describe

_____ as a person who is: _____

_____

_____

The *Real* Me . . . Do You *Know* Me?
The *Real* Me?

Quiet and Shy—Not!

I know there are times when my parents and teachers—even some of my friends—see me differently than I really am. They think I'm quiet and shy, really smart but not very cool. What they don't know is that's who I am when I am with them, but it's not who I really am. The real me comes out when I'm around guys who are more like me—like Tom Henderson and Graham Barry. Tom and Graham bring out the best in me, the real me. We met each other on the first day of the Young Scientist contest last year. Even though the three of us don't get a chance to see each other very often, we're still the best of friends. Tom and Graham know me better than any of the kids at school know me. The three of us just clicked. We really understand each other. I have more fun with them than anyone else. I always feel happy and in a good mood, even when I'm working through a problem, when I talk with Tom and Graham. With them, I'm my "real shade."

—Chad Dalton, 16, *Taste Berries for Teens*

Who understands you—the real you—better than anybody else? How do you know this? Why is it this person is able to understand you? Is it because he or she is just like you, or for some other reason? How long have you known this person? Do you think you will be friends all of your lives?

_____

_____

_____

_____

I find television very educational.
Every time someone switches it on, I go into
another room and read a good book.

—Groucho Marx

Describe a time you felt sure someone "really knew you," and then something happened that made you realize that person didn't know you as well as you thought. For example, did someone ever mistrust you or doubt your word? What happened? What was the incident that showed you this person didn't know the real you? Who was the person? How did you feel about what happened? How did you feel toward the other person?

_____

_____

_____

_____

How did the incident change the relationship between the two of you? Did it strain the friendship, or make it stronger? Are you still friends or did you part company? What did the incident teach you?

_____

_____

_____

_____

Write about a time you felt someone close to you understood you *even better* than you understood yourself. Who was this person? What was the situation or circumstance that brought about this understanding? For example, did this person introduce you to a boyfriend or a girlfriend, whom you never would've considered going out with, but whom you ended up really liking when you found out he or she shared your values and interests?

_____

_____

_____

_____

Who looks outside dreams;
who looks inside wakes.

—C. G. Jung

Taste-Berry Actions:
Getting to Know Me

When someone knows you even better than you know yourself, how does it make you feel about the person? In what ways does it make that person even more special to you?

_____

_____

_____

_____

_____

_____

When someone knows you really well, how can that help you understand or know yourself even better?

_____

_____

_____

_____

_____

_____

_____

If Only You Knew . . .
I'd Like You to Know . . .

Sometimes we need to help our friends get to know "the real me." What two things do you wish all of your friends knew about you? Why *don't* they know? How can you let them know?

1 I wish all my friends knew:

_____

_____

_____

_____

_____

They don't know because:

_____

_____

_____

_____

_____

I can let them know by:

_____

_____

_____

_____

_____

2   I wish all my friends knew:

_____

_____

_____

_____

_____

They don't know because:

_____

_____

_____

_____

_____

I can let them know by:

_____

_____

_____

_____

_____

What two things do you wish all of your family members knew about you? Why don't they know? How can you let them know?

1 I wish all my family members knew:

_____

_____

_____

_____

_____

They don't know because:

_____

_____

_____

_____

_____

I can let them know by:

_____

_____

_____

_____

_____

2   I wish all my family members knew:

_____

_____

_____

_____

_____

They don't know because:

_____

_____

_____

_____

_____

I can let them know by:

_____

_____

_____

_____

_____

Taste-Berry Decisions: Great Expectations

When you're a teenager,
you get pulled in a lot of different
directions, especially when you're trying to meet
the expectations of different people—all
of whom are important to you.

—JENNIFER LEIGH YOUNGS, *TASTE BERRIES FOR TEENS*

Name the five people whose expectations of you matter the most to you. Next to the person's name, describe what it is he or she expects of you.

EXAMPLE:

<u>Who:</u> My Mom.

<u>Expectation:</u> She expects me to be a good student.

<u>How I feel about meeting this expectation:</u> I want to get good grades, too, and I'm glad she believes that I'm smart enough to get them. Still, the added pressure of knowing how disappointed she'll be if I don't do well really stresses me out.

EXAMPLE:

<u>Who:</u> My friend Debbie.

<u>Expectation:</u> She expects me to be her friend, even when she does things I don't like, such as always expecting me to let her copy my homework.

<u>How I feel about meeting this expectation:</u> I feel uncomfortable when I have to just go along with things I don't feel right about—like with copying my homework, sometimes I don't mind, but sometimes I do.

<u>Who:</u> _____

<u>Expectation:</u> _____

_____

_____

_____

<u>How I feel about meeting this expectation:</u> _____

_____

_____

_____

<u>Who:</u> _____

<u>Expectation:</u> _____

_____

_____

_____

The *Real* Me . . . Do You *Know* Me?
The *Real* Me?

How I feel about meeting this expectation: _____

_____

_____

_____

Who: _____

Expectation: _____

_____

_____

_____

How I feel about meeting this expectation: _____

_____

_____

_____

Think it, talk it,
Live it, show it.
What ever you want,
Let the universe know it!

—MICHAEL DOOLEY

Taste-Berry Decisions:
Great Expectations

Who: _____

Expectation: _____

_____

_____

_____

How I feel about meeting this expectation: _____

_____

_____

_____

Who: _____

Expectation: _____

_____

_____

_____

How I feel about meeting this expectation: _____

_____

_____

_____

Do you think it's good that others have expectations for us?
Why?

_____

_____

_____

_____

_____

_____

_____

_____

_____

_____

_____

_____

*Birds make great sky-circles
of their freedom. How do they learn it?
They fall, and falling,
are given wings.*

—RUMI

Taste-Berry Actions:
What I Expect of Others

With so many people to please, we can feel as if every-one has more say-so in our lives than we do. Always doing the things they expect of us can make us feel as if we are not true to ourselves (even though this may not be a fact). It helps to realize that expectations are a part of almost all relationships.

Just as others "expect" things of you, you have expec-tations of them. For example, you expect your parents to buy groceries and to prepare food to eat.

List four people from whom you expect things. What do you expect from each of them? What do you think they think about meeting these expectations?

EXAMPLE:

Who: My boyfriend Eric.

Expectation: I want Eric to make plans for us to go somewhere or do something together every weekend.

How I think my boyfriend feels about meeting this expectation: I think Eric almost always wants us to do something together on the weekend, too; although sometimes he might wish he could skip a weekend and just hang out with his friends.

EXAMPLE:

Who: My little sister Sammy.

Expectation: When my friends come over to my house after

school to do homework or just to hang out, I expect my little sister to understand that I'm entitled to spend some private time with them without her hanging around with us, and that excluding her doesn't mean we don't like her.

How I think my little sister feels about meeting this expectation: I think it's hard for my little sister to understand that I'm entitled to spend time alone with my friends, especially when she looks up to me and my friends and loves to be around us older girls.

Who: _____

Expectation: _____

_____

_____

_____

_____

How I think _____ feels about meeting

this expectation: _____

_____

_____

_____

Who: _____

Expectation: _____

_____

_____

_____

_____

How I think _____ feels about meeting
this expectation: _____

_____

_____

_____

♥

Learn from the past, live in the present,
plan for the future.

—Carushka

Who: _____

Expectation: _____

_____

_____

_____

_____

How I think _____ feels about meeting
this expectation: _____

_____

_____

_____

Who: _____

Expectation: _____

_____

_____

_____

_____

How I think _____ feels about meeting

this expectation: _____

_____

_____

_____

Do you think it's good that we have expectations for others? Why?

_____

_____

_____

_____

_____

Taste-Berry Decisions: Meeting Others Halfway

You and your good friend have made plans to do something together—just the two of you—on Friday evening. Then at the last minute your friend calls you and explains that a "special someone" phoned and your friend has extended an invitation for that person to "come along."

Would you:

1. Tell your friend to phone his or her "special some-one" and explain that the evening has been set up with just the two of you in mind and the two of them should make plans for a different evening?
2. Tell your friend that the two of you can reschedule your plans for spending the evening together at another time?
3. Find a way to meet each other halfway—to compromise?

Explain the reason for your decision.

_____

_____

_____

_____

_____

_____

Compromising is about meeting others "halfway." How could you strike a deal in the situation above?

_____

_____

_____

_____

Are you good at compromising? Or, do you find you always give in and allow the other person to do what he or she would like, even if it means your needs aren't met. Or, do you insist on having your way, sometimes even at the expense of the other person's needs?

Describe a time when you had to meet someone halfway. What was going on? What were you being asked to do? Who was involved? What happened?

_____

_____

_____

_____

_____

_____

_____

_____

_____

_____

How did things turn out? Did everyone "win"? Did everyone get his or her needs met? How do you know?

_____

_____

_____

_____

_____

How did you feel about the outcome? How did the other person feel about the outcome? How did having everyone get his or her needs met contribute to your positive feelings of self?

_____

_____

_____

_____

_____

Your family is having relatives over for your little brother's birthday, and you've been asked to attend a really special party for a good friend. What compromise would you propose to your parents?

_____

_____

_____

_____

Explain how your willingness to meet others halfway was good for everyone involved.

_____

_____

_____

_____

Do you find it easier to meet some friends—more so than others —halfway? Why do you think this is so?

_____

_____

_____

_____

_____

_____

_____

*The most important
trip you take in life is meeting
others halfway.*

—HENRY BOYLE

List two people with whom you find it easy to compromise and explain why it's easy for you to meet each person halfway.

Person: _____

Why it's easy to meet this person halfway: _____

_____

_____

_____

_____

_____

_____

_____

Person: _____

Why it's easy to meet this person halfway: _____

_____

_____

_____

_____

_____

_____

_____

Taste-Berry Actions: Drawing the Line

*Sometimes, there's a fine line
between going along, doing the things
others want you to do, and being true to yourself
—listening to your own voice and preferences,
acting on what you believe, and doing
what's important and best for you.*

—TASTE BERRIES FOR TEENS

What does this quote mean to you?

_____

_____

_____

_____

_____

_____

_____

_____

_____

_____

_____

Where do you draw the line between doing what others want and being true to yourself? Write about a time you were "true to your own color"—the self you know better than anyone else does—though you knew that someone special wouldn't think you were cool for making the choice you did. What was the situation? What was going on? Why weren't you and the other person in agreement? How did you stick up for yourself?

✝ _____

_____

_____

_____

_____

_____

How did things turn out? How did what happened affect the relationship between the two of you? Did your friend think you were a "loser" for not going along with him or her, or did that person admire you for sticking with your decision, regardless of how he or she felt about it? How did that make you feel?

_____

_____

_____

_____

_____

_____

_____

Self-Worth: What You Think of You

Self-worth—what we think
about ourselves—shows up in the things
we say and do. We may even misinterpret the
words and actions of others because
of the view we hold of ourselves.

—*Taste Berries for Teens*

What does this quote mean to you?

_____

_____

_____

_____

How does your self-worth show up in the things you say and do? List two ways.

Example: I think of myself as a good student, so I finish my homework every day.

Example: I think of myself as shy, so I don't always talk to people.

1 _____

_____

_____

2 _____

_____

_____

Using these two examples, how does the view you hold of yourself show up in the way you feel others think of you?

Example: I think of myself as a poor student, so when the teacher doesn't call on me, I think it's because she sees me as not having the right answer. But in fact, she could think I always have the right answer, so she wants to give some other student a chance.

Example: I think of myself as outgoing, so when someone waves in my direction, I just know they're waving at me—when in fact they could be waving at the person behind me.

1 _____

_____

_____

2 _____

_____

_____

The sky will bow to your
beauty if you do.

—RUMI

Taste-Berry Decisions:
Being Your Personal Best

Ferrari, Anyone?

A young boy came home crying from school one day. His grandfather was visiting and greeted him. "Why are you crying?" his grandfather asked. "Because Paul called me a sissy! Do you think I'm a sissy, Grandpa?"

"Oh no," said his grandfather. "I think you're a Ferrari."

"A car?" said the boy, trying to make sense of what his grandfather had said.

"Well, if you believe that just because Paul called you a sissy that you really are one, you might as well believe you're a car, and a terrific one at that," explained the grandfather, asking, "Why be a sissy when you can be a Ferrari?"

"Oh! That's cool, Grandpa!" the boy exclaimed, now realizing that he got to have a say in how he felt about himself. "Yes, it is," replied his grandfather. "The opinion you have of yourself should not only count as much as anyone's—but even more."

—Taste Berries for Teens

Seeing yourself in the most positive light—believing and trusting in you—can help you do better and to "be" a better person. When things are going good, it's pretty easy to have a positive attitude about yourself. But when the going gets tough, it is also important to believe and trust that you can make it through. Staying positive can be a big help.

Write about a time when things weren't going your way and you decided to look on the bright side. What was going on?

_____

_____

_____

_____

_____

_____

Why weren't things going your way? Who was involved? How did your positive attitude and believing in yourself make a difference in the way things turned out?

_____

_____

_____

_____

_____

_____

Taste-Berry Decisions:
Being a Positive Person

I Wouldn't Go Out with
Belinda Even If . . .

Brian had been out of school for three days with the flu. On the morning of his return, he noticed a group of friends clustered around talking about Belinda, the "new girl" at school. All of his friends said how cute and fun she was, and how much they were looking forward to sitting with her at the next day's sports assembly. Even though Brian had no idea who Belinda was, he began his usual habit of being critical of others. "I don't think she's all that cute," he remarked. "She's got skinny legs, and my little sister's got bigger boobs than she does. And she ought to get a new hairstyle!"

Though his friends looked on in disbelief, neither their looks of surprise nor expressions of disgust could deter Brian from making even more disparaging remarks about Belinda—whom he knew nothing about. When Brian announced, "I wouldn't go out on a date with Belinda even if she paid me," one girl in the group, Peggy (a girl Brian secretly liked and hoped to ask out), quipped, "Brian, you are really a geek! And don't worry, no one I know—including Belinda—would go out with you, even if you paid her!" Having said that, she turned and walked away.

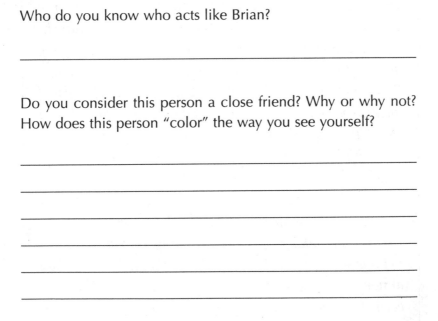

Belinda, the one Brian thought needed a bigger bosom, shapelier legs and a more modern hairstyle, the one Brian was too good to date (even if she paid him), was the new school mascot . . . a goat! Making sure we don't "vandalize" others can be a real "taste berry"—to ourselves and to others!

—Jennifer Leigh Youngs, *Taste Berries for Teens*

Who do you know who acts like Brian?

_____

Do you consider this person a close friend? Why or why not? How does this person "color" the way you see yourself?

_____

_____

_____

_____

_____

_____

*Whoever can see through
all fear will be safe.*

—*Tao Te Ching*

Write about a time when you saw someone being critical of someone you knew. What was happening? Where did this occur? Who was involved? Why was this person being critical?

_____

_____

_____

_____

How did it make you feel to be around someone who was critical—even though it wasn't you this person was criticizing? How did it influence you? What did you do? Did you say anything to the person who was being critical? Did you say anything to the person being criticized? Why? Then what happened?

_____

_____

_____

_____

_____

How did you feel about yourself for what you did or didn't do? How did this contribute to your sense of self?

_____

_____

_____

_____

Taste-Berry Actions:
Being a Positive Person

Write about a time when you stuck up for someone—even though you didn't know that person all that well. What was going on? What were the circumstances? Where did the incident take place? Who was being critical and why? Why did you stick up for the person being criticized?

_____

_____

_____

_____

_____

_____

_____

How did the person being critical feel about what you did? Were you with friends at the time, or alone? If you were with friends, did they side with you or remain neutral?

_____

_____

_____

_____

_____

_____

How did you feel about yourself for doing what you did? How did this contribute to your positive sense of self?

_____

_____

_____

_____

_____

_____

_____

How do you think your friends felt about what you did? In what ways were your actions influential—what did they "teach" others?

_____

_____

_____

_____

_____

_____

_____

Taste-Berry Decisions:
Believing in Yourself

I like it when other people encourage me.
So it only makes sense that I encourage me, too.
It helps me to feel better about myself
and then I actually do better.

—DAN BELANA, 17, *TASTE BERRIES FOR TEENS*

How does feeling better about yourself actually help you do better?

_____

_____

_____

_____

_____

_____

_____

_____

_____

_____

_____

_____

How do you encourage and root for yourself? Write five positive things you can do to encourage yourself.

Examples: When I have a bad day, I remind myself of all the things that were positive in my day.

Examples: When something doesn't turn out the way I planned (and it's because I've goofed up), I tell myself I'm going to work on doing better, and I trust myself to keep working toward my personal best.

★ _____

_____

★ _____

_____

★ _____

_____

★ _____

_____

★ _____

_____

Learning . . . Growing . . . Changing . . . Becoming

As we go about our lives, learning and growing, we keep changing or re-creating ourselves, each creation moving closer to who we really are. We already hold a picture of that person in our minds.

Close your eyes and picture yourself in your mind's eye. Who are you? Think of the best "you" that you can imagine and then describe this "you."

WHO I Am . . . Who I REALLY Am . . . Who I Am

_____

_____

_____

_____

_____

_____

*The work of life is to grow closer
to who we really are, closer to the image
of the person we know ourselves
to be deep down.*

—TASTE BERRIES FOR TEENS

PART 2

Friends:
A Necessity
of Life

*Each friend represents
a world in us, a world possibly
not born until they arrive.*

—Anaïs Nin

Friends: A Necessity of Life

Elephants and Friends Have a Lot in Common

When an elephant is ill or injured, other elephants in the herd gather around to protect the animal and to bolster it up. They know how important their support is because if an elephant in such a condition lays down, it won't be able to stand up again on its own. So, the other members of the herd literally surround their weak friend and help it remain standing. Even when on the move, the other buddies walk next to the ailing elephant, supporting it as they travel.

Just as elephants intuitively know when one of their friends needs assistance, they also know when that friend no longer needs support, and so, they gradually give the elephant a little more room until it walks and functions on its own.

Animals, like people, intuitively know when one of their friends needs their help and support.

—Taste Berries for Teens

A good friend is someone who understands us, some-one we can count on, someone who helps us through tough times, someone we can be ourselves with and have fun with. That's why friends are *friends*.

How would you define a *good* friend?

_____

_____

_____

_____

_____

♥   ♥   ♥   ♥   ♥

What are the five most important qualities you look for in a friend?

1 _____

2 _____

3 _____

4 _____

5 _____

Taste Berries:
The Importance of Friends

Why is it important to you to have friends?

_____

_____

_____

_____

_____

_____

How is having "friends" different from having a "best friend"?

_____

_____

_____

_____

_____

_____

When I'm with you,
I feel secure, whole and so free.
—PEGGY NUNZIATA, 16

A friend is someone with whom
I can reveal many parts of me, even those
I am meeting for the first time.
—JENNIFER LEIGH YOUNGS, *TASTE BERRIES FOR TEENS*

What does this quote mean to you?

_____

_____

_____

_____

As a result of having friends, what "new parts of you" have you met for the first time?

_____

_____

_____

_____

_____

_____

The Difference Between a Friend and a *Best* Friend

*A best friend, whether a guy or a girl,
becomes the "best" friend because that person
makes it safe to be yourself, and to reveal
your own cracks and flaws.*

—TASTE BERRIES FOR TEENS

What does this quote mean to you?

_____

_____

_____

_____

_____

Who is your very best friend? How long has this person been your "best" friend? What is he or she like? Describe your *best friend.*

_____

_____

_____

_____

_____

Why is that person's friendship important to you? How does that person make it "safe for you to be yourself"? What is the most intimate "crack and flaw" you've shared with your best friend?

_____

_____

_____

_____

_____

_____

Do you think this person will be your best friend for always, or just for now?

_____

_____

_____

_____

_____

_____

_____

My Best Friend's Best Traits

What is it about your best friend that you like the most? List five traits about that person that makes him or her special to you.

1 _____
_____
_____

2 _____
_____
_____

3 _____
_____
_____

4 _____
_____
_____

5 _____
_____
_____

A good friend listens. And hears you.

—JENNA REYNOLDS, 15

A Letter to My Best Friend

Most friends write notes back and forth between each other, sharing information about the many things going on in their lives. If you were to write a letter to your best friend thanking him or her for the ways he or she is special to you, what would it say?

_____

_____

_____

_____

_____

_____

_____

_____

_____

_____

_____

We write to taste life twice,
in the moment and in retrospection.

—ANAÏS NIN

Taste Berries:
Who Considers You "Best Friend"?

Who considers you his or her best friend? How do you know this? Why do you think the friendship the two of you share is important to your friend? What's in it for him or her?

? _____

_____

_____

_____

What two things do you think your friend would list as your best friendship qualities?

1 _____

_____

_____

2 _____

_____

_____

You will be my friend—forever.
—CHELSEA SUDBERRY, 17

My Best Friend's Worst Traits

It's only natural to see the positive qualities in our friends and to downplay the "negatives." For example, maybe your best friend smokes and though you know this is bad for her health, you tell yourself that your friend will grow tired of smoking and give it up soon—even though you know smoking is an addiction and it will take some doing for your friend to break her habit.

What are your friend's three worst traits and how have you "explained them away"—making the choice to have this person as your best friend regardless of their "worst traits"?

Worst trait: _____

How I explain it away: _____

_____

Worst trait: _____

How I explain it away: _____

_____

Worst trait: _____

How I explain it away: _____

_____

When you realize there is nothing lacking,
the world belongs to you.

—*Tao Te Ching*

Taste-Berry Breakups . . .
Taste-Berry Makeups

Write about a time you had a major disagreement with your best friend. When did it occur? What caused the argument? Was anyone else involved? Was anyone "in the wrong"?

?
_____

_____

_____

_____

_____

How were you able to resolve your differences? Who made the first move to make up and repair the friendship—you or your friend?

_____

_____

_____

_____

_____

The soft overcomes the hard, the
gentle overcomes the rigid.

—*TAO TE CHING*

If your friend made the first move to repair the rift, were you impressed with the way he or she "rescued" the friendship? Did you feel it was an honest attempt to save the friendship? Or, did you feel the person didn't really want to work through what went wrong, but the two of you drifted back together anyway?

_____

_____

_____

_____

_____

_____

Did the "makeup" include an explanation as to what went wrong, or was it simply an "I'm sorry" but the two of you didn't really talk out why there were hurt feelings in the first place? Exactly what did the other person—or you—say or do to make up?

_____

_____

_____

_____

_____

_____

_____

Taste-Berry Actions:
Working Through Disagreements

How did being at odds with your friend make you feel? How were you affected by the breakup? For example, did you go about your life certain that everything would work out in the end? Did you give your friend a little space and not get too worked up over it? Or were you so upset that you couldn't sleep, were irritable and neglected your responsibilities—such as homework and chores? Or did you write, phone or talk with him or her in person to try to resolve the matter as quickly as possible?

_____

_____

_____

_____

_____

Do you and your friend often have disagreements? If so, who usually starts them, or is it hard to tell?

_____

_____

_____

_____

How do you interpret a disagreement? For example, do you think it's a sign that something is "wrong" with the two of you being friends? Or, do you think that the two of you have come upon an issue where you each want the other to know that you feel strongly about the way you want it handled and it's necessary to stand by your opinion?

_____

_____

_____

_____

_____

_____

_____

_____

Sometimes a disagreement is seemingly petty and after it's over, you wonder why you made such a big deal of it in the first place. And sometimes a disagreement can be a good way to "clear the air," to talk about an issue that the two of you need to discuss. Think back over a recent upset. What did it teach you about yourself? What were you surprised to learn?

EXAMPLE:

I discovered that: I was lonely without her friendship.

I was surprised that: I was so sad. I was surprised how it made me extra-sensitive and kind to others, like I didn't want them to hurt like I was. Like I wanted them to be as kind to me as I needed them to be because I was hurting.

EXAMPLE:

<u>I discovered that:</u> I gossiped about my friend, trying to win our other friends over to my side.

<u>I was surprised that:</u> I could betray someone I once felt so close to. And that I would resort to that sort of behavior (because when I see others do this, I always think it's not very becoming).

<u>I discovered that:</u> _____

_____

<u>I was surprised that:</u> _____

_____

_____

<u>I discovered that:</u> _____

_____

<u>I was surprised that:</u> _____

_____

_____

<u>I discovered that:</u> _____

_____

<u>I was surprised that:</u> _____

_____

_____

I discovered that: _____

_____

I was surprised that: _____

_____

_____

I discovered that: _____

_____

I was surprised that: _____

_____

_____

I discovered that: _____

_____

I was surprised that: _____

_____

_____

Courage is the price that life
exacts for granting peace.
—AMELIA EARHART

Do You Have More than One Best Friend?

If You Really Want to Know

Kayla and Sara are both friends of mine, but they're very different. For instance, the other day the three of us were going to go to the movies. "Do I look okay?" I asked Sara.

Without even so much as looking at me, she replied, "Yeah, sure. You always look great."

"How about my hair?"

"Yeah. Looks great," she responded. The moment Kayla walked in, she took one look at me and demanded, "You're not going to be seen in that, are you? No way am I going to be seen with you if you wear that!"

"What's wrong with it?" I asked. "Well, for one thing, you look like a little kid in it, and for another, there's a mustard stain on the left sleeve." She paused, frowned and then added, "Having a bad hair day?"

So you can see how different they are. Sara is a person who doesn't want to upset you, so she always says something nice and would never want to make you feel uneasy, no matter what. Kayla is very blunt and outspoken. She has very definite opinions and isn't afraid to be honest. Kayla is definitely not afraid of what you'll think about what she has to say. So if I really, really want to know how I look, while I ask them both, it's Kayla's advice that's worth the most. She has no problem telling me her honest opinion about anything. If the way I look passes her *inspection, I can be sure that it will pass with others. Now, if I was worried about a big test at school, I'd go to Sara for help. Kayla puts as little energy as possible into her grades. Sara, on the other hand, is very smart, understands what it's like to want to get good grades, and will help you out when you need it. So both Kayla and Sara are good friends, each in her own way.*

Friends. They're so different. That's why you need lots of them.

—Barbara Allen, 14, *Taste Berries for Teens*

Do you have more than one best friend? How many best friends do you have? List the top six.

1. _____

2. _____

3. _____

4. _____

5. _____

6. _____

Does your best friend mind that you have other close friends? How do you know?

_____

_____

_____

_____

_____

In what ways are your friends also friends with each other? For example, do they play on the same sport teams or go to the same school? Are they friends because one of the things they have in common is a friendship with you?

_____

_____

_____

_____

_____

How do you feel about your friends being friends with each other? Is it just fine with you that they all call each other? How about if they call each other, but not you? Is it important to you to know about the relationship they share with each other, or do you feel you all have a right to your privacy?

_____

_____

_____

_____

_____

_____

How Are Your Friends Alike?

In what two ways are your two closest friends alike?

♡ _____

♡ _____

In what two ways are those same two friends different?

♡ _____

♡ _____

Why do you like that your friends are different, or why do you wish they were more alike?

_____

_____

_____

_____

How does having friends who are different from each other make your life more interesting?

_____

_____

_____

_____

Friends: Two's Company.
Is Three a Crowd?

Write about a time when a friend made it clear that he or she was to be your only friend—period! Who was that friend? How did he or she let you know this? Describe the incident or circumstances that brought this about. How did you feel about it, and what did you do? Are you still friends?

_____

_____

_____

_____

_____

_____

_____

_____

_____

_____

The secret to having it all
is loving it all.

—DR. JOYCE BROTHERS

Taste-Berry Decisions:
Having Awesome Friends

For You to Cry In

My grandmother was one of my very favorite people in all the world. Her name was Tilly, but I called her "Grams." Besides being fun to be around, Grams was one of the most positive people I've known. She had a way of making me feel like I was truly special. She believed in me and felt I could do anything I wanted, and that I would. She told everyone that I was "destined to grow up and change the world." With her, I was an "unlimited" person.

But then, when she was only sixty-one years old, Grams died from a brain aneurysm. I had visited her only two days before. She seemed healthy and was her usual, happy self. I was heartsick.

Knowing how much I loved and missed my grandmother, my two best friends did what the herd of elephants did for their sick friend: They rallied around me. Their parents allowed them to stay home from school and go with me to my grandmother's funeral. And the days following my grandmother's death they were so extra kind and sensitive to my feelings. Regularly they asked, "Are you doing okay?" I found that so loving, and it showed me that they understood the hurt I was feeling.

The evening after the funeral, both of them came to my house. They brought me a stuffed animal with a note: "For you to cry in." They both stayed over that night, which was really nice. My friends' empathy toward my sadness was like a big comforting pillow. They really cared and understood. It gave me a sense of friendship that I hadn't really felt from friends before. For sure, my friends helped ease the pain I felt over Grams's death.

I will always miss Grams. She was such a good friend; it showed in everything she did. More than anyone else, it was Grams's "style" of friendship that helps me understand that a friendship is special because of the things that people do to make it special. The relationship between my grandmother and me was special because Grams made a point of making it special—like my friends and I do for each other.

We laugh together, cry together, cheer each other on and commiserate and listen to each other. Like the elephants, we gather around to help each other. And because we do, we each know we can count on the other—in good times and in bad.

—Roma Kipling, 17, *Taste Berries for Teens*

Do you have an adult friend as close and loving as "Grams"? Who?

_____

_____

Can your parents, grandparents, or even brothers or sisters be a "close" friend? Why do you feel this way?

_____

_____

_____

Friends: Helping You Cope
with Tough Times

Describe an incident when a friend helped you cope with a really tough time. How old were you? What were you going through? Who was the friend? In what ways did your friend help you get through this time? What did he or she do that was so helpful?

_____

_____

_____

_____

_____

Did the support you got from your friend surprise you, or did you expect that he or she would respond in this way?

_____

_____

_____

_____

Good friends, good books.
This is the ideal life.

—Mark Twain

Taste-Berry Friends:
Coping with Tough Times

How did the way your friend responded to you during this tough time change the relationship you share? For example, did it strengthen your bond (or did it tear it apart); do you talk more frequently now; do you trust each other implicitly; do you know where each other is "coming from"?

_____

_____

_____

_____

_____

_____

How long have you and this person been friends? Are you and this person still friends? Do you think you will be friends your entire lives?

_____

_____

_____

_____

_____

Friends and Secrets . . .
Deep, Dark Secrets

A good friend is someone with
whom we can relax and just hang out,
have fun and share our innermost thoughts—
deep dark secrets, lofty and noble goals,
or our hopes, joys and fears.

—TASTE BERRIES FOR TEENS

Have you ever shared a secret with your best friend? Did your friend also share a secret, or just you? How long had this person been your friend before you shared your secret?

_____

_____

_____

_____

How many secrets do you and your best friend have between you? What is the best secret you have ever shared with a good friend?

_____

_____

_____

_____

Friends and Secrets . . .
And Promises to Keep

Have you ever had a friend promise to keep a secret and then break that promise? Why did your friend break the trust? What happened as a result?

_____

_____

_____

_____

Did you and your friend ever forgive each other? Exactly what was said between the two of you?

_____

_____

_____

_____

Is that person still your friend? How do you feel about that person now?

_____

_____

_____

_____

Have you ever betrayed someone's trust in you to keep a promise? What was the promise? Why did you break the trust? What happened? Who found out? What happened then?

_____

_____

_____

 _____

_____

_____

_____

How did you feel about yourself for breaking the trust? How did doing this change the friendship?

_____

_____

_____

_____

_____

_____

*If you want something, release the wish
and let it light on its desire.*

—RUMI

Taste-Berry Decisions . . .
Having Good Friends

What secret is so big you never told anyone, not even your best friend? Why haven't you told a single soul? Is it because the secret feels too terrible to reveal, or that you don't have a friend whom you trust to keep your secret?

_____

_____

_____

_____

_____

_____

How does it feel to not be able to share it with anyone? Do you think someday you will share it with a special someone? Who do you think that person will be: your mom or dad, a boyfriend or girlfriend, someone you've yet to meet?

_____

_____

_____

_____

_____

_____

Taste-Berry Friends: Being a Good Listener

My Stand-In Brother

One day my seven-year-old brother, Tim, col-lapsed on the school playground and was rushed to the hospital, where he lay in a coma. When I saw my brother hooked up to the wires and tubes, I felt sick to my stomach. It was scary. I didn't know what all the tubes were supposed to do, but I did know Timmy needed them to stay alive. There was nothing that I or anyone else could do. We just had to wait.

My parents stayed at the hospital with Timmy as much as they could. Since I had to go to school, my mother called the parents of my friend, Stephen, and asked if I could stay with them until Timmy got better. They said I could stay as long as was needed.

Each day right after school, Stephen's mother took me to the hospital to see my brother. Stephen came along. Seeing my brother in the hospital bed covered in all those wires and tubes never got easier. Even just being in the room made me sad. My parents were so upset that it hurt to look at them. Soon I didn't want to go to the hospital unless Stephen went with me. Seeing my brother must have frightened Stephen, too, but he always went with me and never complained about it.

All the nights my brother was in the hospital, I didn't sleep very well, but one night was the worst. I was crying and it woke up Stephen. He asked me if he should get his parents. I thought that showed understanding. I told him that I didn't need his parents, that it was just that I had a nightmare that Timmy had died. When I told Stephen more about the nightmare, he didn't think I was weird. He just listened. And even though I started crying, he didn't tell me not to. And he didn't pretend that everything was going to be alright. Stephen just said he was sorry that my brother was so sick and that he was scared for him, too.

We started talking about dying and what that must be like. It helped that I could be honest about everything I was feeling. Stephen nodded in perfect understanding, and then he said, "I hope Timmy doesn't die. But if he does, and you ever need a brother, I'll be your stand-in brother."

My parents called very early the next morning for me to come to the hospital. When I got there, they told me that my brother had died. Now, on those times when I miss Timmy the most, or just need to remember Timmy by talking about him, I know who to call: Stephen, my stand-in brother. He's always there for me to talk to. And many times, just to listen.

—Curt Lindholm, 15, *Taste Berries for Teens*

Who among your friends is most like Stephen? How long have you been friends? Do you think you will be friends your entire lives? Why do you think this?

_____

_____

_____

Taste-Berry Actions: Listening

*A good friend is someone who
allows you a safe space to share your deepest
thoughts and needs—without worry
of being judged, criticized or made to feel silly
for feeling the way you do.*

—*Taste Berries for Teens*

What does this quote mean to you?

_____

_____

_____

_____

Caring enough to show compassion for what others are going through is an important part of being a friend. Write about a time one of your friends showed you compassion. What was going on for you at the time? What did your friend do? How did your friend give you a "safe space" and allow you to express yourself freely—to be sad, to cry, to be disappointed, to be angry?

_____

_____

_____

_____

_____

_____

_____

_____

_____

_____

_____

How did it feel to be able to go through all the things that you needed to feel, knowing you wouldn't lose the friendship? Are you still friends?

_____

_____

_____

_____

_____

_____

_____

_____

Taste-Berry Friends: Being *Real*

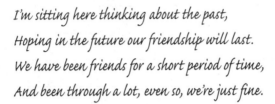

Our Friendship Is Real

I'm sitting here thinking about the past,
Hoping in the future our friendship will last.
We have been friends for a short period of time,
And been through a lot, even so, we're just fine.

I've seen lots of people come and go,
Saying and doing whatever—careless, you know?
That's why your friendship means so much to me,
When I'm with you, I feel secure, whole, and so free.

Free from those who won't be around,
When times get tough, and I am down.
You'll be there for me and understand how I feel,
Because we both know our friendship is real.

—Peggy Nunziata, 16, *Taste Berries for Teens*

How can you tell if a friendship is "real"?

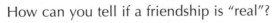

_____

_____

_____

_____

_____

_____

_____

_____

_____

_____

_____

Intimacies between women go backwards,
beginning with revelations and
ending up with small talk.

—ELIZABETH BOWEN

How to Tell If Your Friendship Is Real

Describe an incident that tested your friendship—one that really showed you *if* your friend was *really* your friend. What happened? What was the issue that tested the friendship? Who was involved? How did you feel about what was going on?

_____

_____

_____

_____

_____

How did things turn out in the end? Are you still friends?

_____

_____

_____

_____

Do you think it's good to test your friendship now and then to see if your friend is still loyal to you? Or do you think, as a friend of ours once said, "You can burn out a battery by testing it"?

_____

_____

_____

_____

Do you think that a good friend needs to "test" the relationship or would that imply maybe you aren't as good friends as you had hoped?

_____

_____

_____

Is there a difference between "testing" and "pressure"? For example, if a boyfriend or girlfriend tries to pressure you into having sex by saying, "But you would if you loved me!" or tried to talk you into doing something you didn't want to do by saying, "You would if you were my friend," would you call that pressure or testing the relationship?

_____

_____

_____

_____

Describe a time when you knew someone was testing your friendship. Why did this person do this? How did things turn out? Is that person still your friend? Did the "testing" make your friendship stronger and more "real" or did it strain it?

_____

_____

_____

_____

Taste-Berry Decisions:
Being a "Real" Friend

Do you think it's possible for someone to be a "real" friend without being a close friend? Whom do you consider a "real" friend, even though you aren't close friends, and why?

☞ _____

_____

_____

_____

List three "real" friends you can count on and describe what it is each one does to let you know you can trust him or her to be there for you.

★ A Real Friend: _____

How I know this person is my friend: _____

_____

_____

_____

_____

★ A Real Friend: _____

How I know this person is my friend: _____

_____

_____

_____

_____

⭐ A Real Friend: _____

How I know this person is my friend: ___ _____

_____

_____

_____

_____

What one person more than anyone else taught you the most important lesson about being a good friend? What was the lesson? Why was it so meaningful to you? What did you learn from this lesson? How do you feel about the person who taught this lesson?

_____

_____

_____

_____

_____

_____

_____

_____

_____

The Rules of Friendship: *My* Rules

Did I Pass Your Test for Friends?

I try to read your eyes,

surmise,

just what you think behind that brow.

As you nod,

are you thinking that I am odd?

You seem not to be impressed

at what you see;

I am

a nonentity?

You're in a hurry to forget,

What made me second-class?

I see I didn't pass the standards you have set

for friends.

So our story ends.

—Elmer Adrian, 93, *Taste Berries for Teens*

What are the rules for being your friend? For example, do you expect your friends to stick up for you even when you are in the wrong? Do you expect a good friend to compliment you when you do something especially good, like ace an exam, or look extra nice? What are five of the most basic "rules" you expect someone to "pass" in order to be your friend?

Rule #1: _____

_____

_____

_____

Rule #2: _____

_____

_____

_____

Rule #3: _____

_____

_____

_____

Rule #4: _____

_____

_____

_____

Rule #5: _____

_____

_____

_____

The Rules of Friendship:
My Rules, Your Rules

Do your friends have rules for being their friend? Do you feel they are pretty much like your "rules" or are they very different?

➤ _____

_____

_____

List three of the rules your best friend has for the friendship the two of you share.

Rule #1: _____

_____

_____

_____

Rule #2: _____

_____

_____

_____

Rule #3: _____

_____

_____

_____

How do you know these rules are understood? For example, did you and your friend talk about them, or are they just unwritten rules that are understood?

_____

_____

_____

_____

When was the last time one of these rules was clarified? How was that done—was it discussed, or did someone get upset with you because you violated the expected "code of conduct"?

_____

_____

_____

_____

Do the rules for friendship apply across the board: Are they the same for "regular" friends as they are for "best" friends? How do you know? Describe an incident that showed you they were the same, or different.

_____

_____

_____

_____

_____

Taste-Berry Decisions:
To Be or Not to Be Your Friend

Is it possible to be friends with everyone, or do you think that some people make better friends than others? Is it possible for some people to be "good" for us, while others are "bad" for us? How do you know when a friend is right for you, while another is not?

_____

_____

_____

_____

_____

_____

Did you ever have a friend who was a bad influence on you? Who was this person? How could you tell—in what ways was this person a bad influence? Is this person still your friend?

_____

_____

_____

_____

_____

_____

_____

_____

_____

When someone is not right for you, not "good" for you, how do you say "no go" to the friendship? Do you just ignore the person and hope he or she will get the message and stop hanging around you, or do you tell the person directly (or ask your friends to tell the person)?

_____

_____

_____

_____

_____

_____

_____

_____

Better keep yourself clean and bright.
You are the window through which you
must see the world.

—GEORGE BERNARD SHAW

Growing, Going:
Leaving Friendship Behind

Sometimes You Just Outgrow
Your Friends

My older sister is in her first year of junior college and having a great time. So I've decided I want to go to college, too—the same one she's attending.

I haven't always wanted to go to college. My two best friends, Lindy and Rianna, and I had planned to find jobs and share an apartment right after we got out of high school. Now that my plans have changed, I have a bit of a problem. For one thing, my grades haven't been all that great, so I'm going to have to put more time into my studies to make sure I can get accepted to junior college. This means I'm going to have to spend less time with Lindy and Rianna. I'm no longer as interested in being a high school student as I am in becoming a college student.

Lindy and Rianna and I have always spent nearly all our free time together. We go to the arcade every day after school, and sometimes on the weekends. If we're not there, we're at the movies—or somewhere. Lindy and Rianna are a lot of fun to be with. Even so, being with them takes up a lot of my time. While this was once okay, now it's more time than I'm willing to give up.

So the problem is, now that our lives are starting to go in different directions, the friendship is really strained. I'm beginning to spend more time with my sister—and her friends. At first Lindy and Rianna were okay with this, now they seem annoyed. "Are you going with us to the movies on Friday, or are you going to hang out with your preppie friends?" they ask. "What do you mean, you can't go? It's only homework," or "Don't be such a drag." I can tell by their comments that they resent the plans I've made.

I think that when you change, your friends have a hard time with it. Sometimes you can't prevent hard feelings. The sad truth is, sometimes you just outgrow your friends.

—Belinda Carr, 16, *Taste Berries for Teens*

Do you think Belinda is right about that?

_____

_____

_____

_____

Have you ever outgrown a friend? How did you know?

_____

_____

_____

_____

_____

Have You Ever Had to
Leave a Friend Behind?

Write about a time you had to end a friendship. Who was the friend you had to "give up"? How did you know you needed to let the friendship go? Why did you need to give it up—what happened? How did you feel about this?

_____

_____

_____

_____

How did you tell the other person the friendship wasn't right for you any longer? How did the other person feel about this? How did the person respond when you told him or her, or did he or she know it was coming? How did the person feel about things?

_____

_____

_____

_____

*I personally think we developed language because
of our deep, inner need to complain.*

—JANE WAGNER

Taste-Berry Decisions:
Making Friends: New Faces, New Places

Is it easy for you to make new friends or is it scary to you? Would you rather initiate the friendship, or do you prefer the other person show an interest in being your friend first?

_____

_____

_____

_____

How do you know if someone else wants to be your friend? What are the signs?

_____

_____

_____

_____

How can you tell if that person will be right for you as a friend? Can you tell right away, or is it something that comes with time?

_____

_____

_____

_____

What is the best way to be a friend to someone new, someone you don't know very well?

_____

_____

_____

_____

How would you handle it if you really wanted to be friends with someone, but you thought your other friends would disapprove?

_____

_____

_____

_____

Is there someone with whom you would like to become better friends? Who is it? What is it about this person that makes you want to be his or her friend?

_____

_____

_____

_____

_____

List three things you intend to do to get to know this person better.

EXAMPLE:

I would ask him or her if he or she wants to sit with me and some of my friends at the school assembly.

1 _____

_____

_____

2 _____

_____

_____

3 _____

_____

_____

Your source of power is in your freedom to choose.

—LORI GIOVANNONI

A Friend Helps Me Grow into Myself

Friends help us grow into
being who we are.

—JENNIFER LEIGH YOUNGS, *TASTE BERRIES FOR TEENS*

What does it mean to "grow into who we are"?

_____

_____

_____

_____

One of the wonderful things about good friends is that they help us see the good in ourselves. This reaffirms that we are doing the right things, that we are a person who is trying to make the best of our lives and getting through the rough spots in positive ways. In what ways do your friends help you grow into who you are?

_____

_____

_____

_____

Taste-Berry Decisions:
Being My *Own* Best Friend

Sometimes we don't think about friendship as an important relationship that we have with ourselves as well as with others. Yet it's important that we be a good friend to ourselves. If a little voice inside were to share with you ways you are a friend to yourself, what five things would that inner voice say?

EXAMPLE:

Dear Andrea: Thank you for saying *no* to drugs when Scott Bayless offered you a hit at the party Saturday night.

1 _____

_____

_____

_____

2 _____

_____

_____

_____

3 _____

_____

_____

_____

_____

4 _____

_____

_____

_____

5 _____

_____

_____

_____

We meet ourselves time and time again in a
thousand disguises on the path of life.

—C. G. Jung

Taste-Berry Actions:
Being My Own Best Friend

Just as a little voice thanked you for treating yourself kindly, what five requests would it make? In what ways would you like to treat yourself even better?

EXAMPLE:

Dear Andrea: Please eat breakfast. I get so tired before lunch when you don't.

1 _____

_____

_____

2 _____

_____

3 _____

_____

4 _____

_____

5 _____

_____

Becoming a Taste Berry:
Being My Own Friend

Being a good friend to yourself makes you a good friend to others. List three ways in which being a good friend to yourself makes you a better friend to others.

EXAMPLE:

It makes me feel good about myself so I have a more positive outlook to share with my friends.

1 _____

_____

_____

2 _____

_____

_____

3 _____

_____

_____

Always remember *you* are your own best friend. Friends may come and go but *you* will be there to face yourself. *You* will be there for yourself with the consequences of your choices—good and bad. *You* will be alone with *you*. So treat yourself with respect and the love you deserve!

PART 3

The Power of Love

*There is one happiness
in life, to love and
be loved.*

—George Sand

Love: An Irresistible Desire to Be Irresistibly Desired!

Love is the irresistible desire
to be irresistibly desired.

—ROBERT FROST

What do you think Robert Frost had in mind when he penned this quote?

Do you think the desire to be irresistibly desired is a universal feeling, felt by everyone, young and old alike, or that not everyone has a need to experience love in this way?

Do you feel "irresistibly desired" by your mom and dad?

_____

Would your parents say that they feel "irresistibly desired" by you?

_____

Who besides your family is "in love" with you?

_____

How does it feel (or how do you think it feels) to be, in Robert Frost's words, "irresistibly desired"?

? _____

_____

_____

_____

Are you in love with anyone? Is anyone in love with you?

♥ _____

_____

_____

_____

_____

The Power of Love in Our Lives

*Being loved affirms that we are lovable,
worth loving. Giving love gives us
purpose—we are needed.*

—TASTE BERRIES FOR TEENS

What does this quote mean to you?

_____ _____

_____

_____

_____

Is it possible to have too much love in our lives? Is it possible to not have enough?

_____

_____

_____

_____

If someone asked you why having love in our lives is important, what would you say? What is the best thing about *feeling* love?

_____

_____

_____

_____

What is the *source* of love? Is it a learned thing, or are we just
born with a capacity to love?

_____

_____

If someone grows up without feeling loved, will he or she turn
out to be a loving person anyway, or is that not possible?

_____

_____

_____

_____

*Love has been called the most potent force in all the
world. There's no greater force for good, no greater
power for creating change in our lives.*

—*Taste Berries for Teens*

What does this quote mean to you?

_____

_____

_____

_____

Have you ever "changed" in the name of love? Who did you change for? Why? How did you change?

_____

_____

_____

_____

How does being a loving person act as a "force for good" in your life? For example, does it make you more patient, more tolerant, more forgiving, more open-minded? How does it "color" the way you see yourself and others?

_____

_____

_____

_____

Do you think if we all do our part to "love enough" that we could make the world an even better place in which to live? When all people learn to love each other more than they already do, how will the world be different than it is now? Do you think people the world over are showing more love and tolerance for each other than they did, say, ten years ago? Why?

_____

_____

_____

_____

Taste-Berry Actions:
Being a Loving Person

If you were trying to explain to your boyfriend or girlfriend—or your best friend—the importance of being a loving and lovable person, what would you say?

_____

_____

_____

_____

_____

_____

What do you think is the difference between being a "loving" person and being a "lovable" person?

_____

_____

_____

_____

All that matters is what we
do for each other.

—Lewis Carroll

Taste Berries:
Who Was Your First Love?

Who was your first love? What was it that made that person so special?

How did you know it was "love" you were feeling? What were the signs?

How did you meet that person? Where did you meet? How old were you? How old was he or she? Is that person still your love?

Did your friends like this person? How do you know? What did
they say?

_____

_____

_____

_____

_____

Did your parents approve? How do you know? What did they say?

_____

_____

_____

_____

_____

Who besides you knew you were in love with this person? Did
you want them to know or were you hoping they wouldn't find
out? Or did you want the entire world to know? Why?

_____

_____

_____

_____

_____

How did they find out? Did you tell them, or wear his or her ring or constantly pal around with that person?

_____

_____

_____

_____

How long did your love last? Are you still in love with this person?

_____

_____

_____

_____

How did loving this person make a difference in your life? Was it a good change? How do you know?

_____

_____

_____

_____

_____

I used to be shy. You made me sing.

—RUMI

How Can You Tell When You Are in Love?

The Heart's Checklist

"Oh Mom," I groaned, "I have a crush on two boys. How will I choose between them?" I was look-ing for a fast, short answer in trying to understand the romantic workings of the heart.

"Oh," she replied. "The heart makes all decisions when it comes to matters of love. The heart knows who to choose."

"But how?" I asked.

"In the right-hand top corner of your heart there is a little checklist of all the things you desire. When you meet someone who possesses the qualities of the things on your list for love, your soul nudges your heart, and you just know," she replied.

Then my mother added the most important words of all: "You must listen carefully to your heart."

—Jennifer Leigh Youngs, *Taste Berries for Teens*

Do you think your heart knows what it wants—maybe even before you do? How do you know?

_____

_____

_____

_____

_____

What is the checklist in your heart? Make a list of all the qualities you would hope to find in a boyfriend or girlfriend. Would
you like that person to be funny, smart, a good listener, cute, a
cat-lover? Be as specific as possible.

✔ _____

✔ _____

✔ _____

✔ _____

✔ _____

✔ _____

✔ _____

✔ _____

✔ _____

✔ _____

✔ _____

✔ _____

✔ _____

✔ _____

✔ _____

✔ _____

✔ _____

✔ _____

Do you *listen* to your heart? For example, when your heart says, "Wow, this feels good," do you think, "I am happy when I am with this person,"? Or when your heart says, "Something about this doesn't feel quite right," do you think, "I am not feeling as happy as I should"? What do you do with the messages your heart gives you?

_____

_____

_____

_____

_____

Does your heart rule you or do you tell your heart what to do? How do you know this?

_____

_____

_____

_____

Do you trust your heart? Do you consider it a wise friend? Does your heart have good instincts? How do you know?

_____

_____

_____

_____

Taste-Berry Actions:
Having a Talk with Your Heart

Do you ever "talk" with your heart? Write a letter to your heart, thanking it for all the love it brings into your life, and if you'd like, ask for even more! You might even use this opportunity to give some special instructions for how you would like it to "behave" in matters of love!

My Dear Heart,

_____

_____

_____

_____

_____

_____

_____

_____

_____

Gamble everything for love if you
are a true human being.

—Rumi

Has Your Heart Ever Asked,
"Is This Right for You"?

Write about a time you liked someone, but it just didn't feel right to your heart. Who was that someone? How did your heart know it wasn't right—how did you feel at the time?

_____

_____

_____

_____

Did you listen to your heart and do what it asked of you? What happened? Is the relationship over, or are you still involved with that person? How do you feel about this?

_____

_____

_____

_____

If you started liking someone new and your heart told you it wasn't right for you, what would you do differently this time?

_____

_____

_____

_____

Write about a time you liked someone, and it felt just right to your heart. Who was that someone? How did your heart know it was right—how did you feel at the time?

_____

_____

_____

_____

Did you listen to your heart and do what it asked of you? What happened? Is the relationship over, or are you still involved with that person? Was your heart right about that person being right for you?

_____

_____

_____

_____

_____

_____

Does this person match your heart's "checklist"? How can you tell?

_____

_____

_____

Can You Love More than One Person at the Same Time?

While you were with someone your heart said was right, if you started liking someone else who your heart also said was right for you, what would you do?

Do you think your heart can like two people at the same time? How do you know?

Have you ever been "in love" with two people at the same time? What was it like? Who were the two people? Did they know about each other? What happened? What did you do? Do you still like both of them? What's your relationship with each of them now?

_____

_____

_____

_____

_____

_____

_____

If someone asked you about how to handle being in love with two people at the same time, what advice would you give them?

♥ ♥ _____

_____

_____

_____

_____

_____

_____

_____

_____

♥   ♥   ♥   ♥   ♥   ♥   ♥   ♥

Taste-Berry Choices: Should You Listen to Your Heart or Head?

The Split

Sometimes my heart
wants something so badly
though my head knows it's wrong
I run after it gladly.

Sometimes my heart
longs for someone so much
that though my head knows it's wrong
I still long for the touch.

My head says
"Your heart is so girlish!"
My heart says
"Your head is so foolish!"

And so I must live
with a heart and a head, you see
who chatter and banter
back and forth as they disagree

While it's left to me
to decide who is right and who is wrong
many times, I can't
So, I just tag along!

—Jennifer Leigh Youngs, *More Taste Berries for Teens*

When it comes to matters of love, your heart and your head can disagree over who is "right" for you. And of course, they may totally agree. But what if there is a split decision? When it comes to love, are your heart and head in sync—or do they "chatter and banter"? How can you tell?

_____

_____

_____

_____

_____

_____

_____

Write about a time your heart and your head disagreed on a matter of love. What was it they disagreed about? Who was it they disagreed over? What happened?

_____

_____

_____

_____

_____

_____

_____

Should You Listen to Your
Heart or Head?

Who "won"—your heart or your head? How do you know? Describe the "battle" that went on between your heart and your head.

♥ _____
_____

_____

_____

_____

_____

_____

How did it turn out? Did you make the best decision? How do you know?

_____

_____

_____

_____

♥ _____

_____

Taste-Berry Choices: Should You Listen to Your Heart or Head?

The heart is forever inexperienced in love.

—Henry David Thoreau

What do you think this quote means? How has it been true or not true for you?

_____

_____

_____

_____

_____

How are you feeling about being a loving person? Do you feel that your heart is "inexperienced" or that you've learned a lot about love—and yourself as well?

_____

_____

_____

_____

Love is the way messengers from
the mystery tell us things.

—RUMI

What do you think this quote means?

_____

_____

_____

_____

_____

_____

_____

Do you think love is a messenger? Do you believe that love is meant to be a mystery or that we are supposed to get it figured out?

_____

_____

_____

_____

_____

_____

The Best Thing About Love . . .

What is the *best* thing about having a boyfriend or girlfriend?

_____

_____

_____

_____

What is the *worst* thing about having a boyfriend or girlfriend?

_____

_____

_____

_____

What do your friends think about your boyfriend or girlfriend?

_____

_____

_____

What do your parents think about your boyfriend or girlfriend?

_____

_____

_____

How Far Will You Go for Love?

How Far I'll Go

How far will I go? Pretty far, when it comes to Sheree.

I asked Sheree to the school dance. She insisted I wear a tux, even though it was black-tie optional. I rented a tux to please her, even though I prefer clothes that are more casual and comfortable.

How far will I go? Pretty far, when it comes to Sheree.

Sheree insisted on arriving at the dance in a limo! I really couldn't afford it, but nevertheless, I worked the extra hours on my part-time job—even though it was finals and I needed the time to study.

How far will I go? Pretty far, when it comes to Sheree.

It was time to sign up for the next semester's schedule. I'd planned to take a third year of Spanish to complete my college entry requirements for a foreign language. But Sheree wanted me to take French with her. "It's so much more romantic," she said. I took French for the sole reason of being in the same class with Sheree.

How far will I go? Pretty far, when it comes to Sheree.

"Let's double-date with my best friend Tom," I suggested. "Let's not," she said. "He's a geek, and besides, I don't like the girl he dates." Sheree had a different circle of friends, so I went places with Sheree and her friends, and I didn't seem to see much of my friends anymore. When it came to going out with friends, we just always seemed to end up with hers.

How far will I go? Pretty far when it comes to Sheree.
Sheree called and said that if I didn't take her to the library, she'd get an F in tomorrow's assignment. I told Sheree I'd made a promise to my father that I'd never take the car without his permission. Despite the fact that I couldn't reach my father until later that evening—and because Sheree was so insistent—I took Sheree to the library.

How far will I go? Six weeks all totaled—that's how far I would go with Sheree! Six weeks into the relationship, I started the new semester with a lie between me and my father, not having seen much of my friends, and a class I didn't need—and without one I did.

How far will I go? Well, pretty far now that I'm not with Sheree. I've learned not to give up the things that are really important to me, the things I value and that make me happy, and move me toward my goals, keeping the promises I make with important people, like friends and my parents.

But that doesn't mean I've signed off on love—I just learned not to ever go that far again.

—Christopher Gillian, 17, *Taste Berries for Teens*

Have you ever "gone too far" for love? How?

_____

_____

_____

_____

_____

Write about a time when you made a decision to do something for love, and you really went too far. How far did you go? What did you do? Who was involved? What were your feelings at the time?

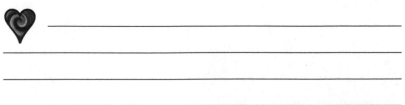

_____

_____

_____

_____

_____

_____

_____

_____

How did things turn out? What happened? How do you feel about the whole thing now?

_____

_____

_____

_____

When you did go too far, what did you learn from the experience?

_____

_____

_____

_____

If you could do one thing over in the entire experience, what would it be?

_____

_____

_____

_____

Have you told anyone about this experience? Who? Why?

_____

_____

_____

_____

To live remains an art
which everyone must learn and
which no one can teach.

—HAVELOCK ELLIS

What do you think Havelock Ellis means by this?

_____

_____

_____

_____

Taste-Berry Decisions:
How Far You'll Go for Love

Write about a time when you made a decision to do something for love, and it turned out just right—the sacrifice was well worth it. What was the decision you made? What was the sacrifice? For example, did you have to become a better student because your boyfriend or girlfriend valued that and expected it of you?

_____

_____

_____

_____

_____

_____

_____

_____

How did it all turn out just right? How did you feel about things?

_____

_____

_____

_____

Taste-Berry Decisions:
How Far You'll Go for Love

List five things that are so important to you that you will *not* give them up for love—no matter what this could mean, for example, your spiritual beliefs, your values, or your time with your friends. Why are each of these so important to you?

♡ What I won't give up: _____

_____

Why it's important to me: _____

_____

_____

♡ What I won't give up: _____

_____

Why it's important to me: _____

_____

_____

♡ What I won't give up: _____

_____

Why it's important to me: _____

_____

_____

♡ What I won't give up: _____

_____

Why it's important to me: _____

_____

_____

♡ What I won't give up: _____

_____

Why it's important to me: _____

_____

_____

What's your "secret" for staying true to yourself no matter who might pressure you to do otherwise?

✝ _____

_____

_____

_____

Love waits on welcome, not on time.

—*A Course in Miracles*

What Is Unconditional Love?

Unconditional love means accepting someone for who he or she is and loving that person in spite of his or her shortcomings. It means believing in and loving that person "no matter what." Yet, we wouldn't allow ourselves to stay in a relationship if it wasn't healthy for us to do so. Loving unconditionally can even mean letting someone go.

What does "unconditional love" mean to you?

_____

_____

_____

_____

_____

_____

_____

Name four people who *love you* unconditionally, and how you know they do.

♡ Who: _____

How I know it: _____

_____

_____

_____

♡ Who: _____

How I know it: _____

_____

_____

_____

♡ Who: _____

How I know it: _____

_____

_____

_____

♡ Who: _____

How I know it: _____

_____

_____

_____

What does it feel like to be loved unconditionally?

_____

_____

_____

_____

How can loving someone unconditionally still mean "letting someone go"—breaking off the friendship?

_____

_____

_____

_____

*Love is what you've been through
with somebody.*

—JAMES THURBER

What does this quote mean to you?

_____

_____

_____

_____

_____

Taste-Berry Decisions:
Letting Go, Moving On

A thousand half-loves must be forsaken
to take one whole heart home.

—RUMI

What do you think this quote means?

_____

_____

_____

_____

Write about a time when you knew a relationship was just not good for you, and so you had to say no to the friendship. Why was the relationship not a good choice for you? Who did you have to "let go"?

_____

_____

_____

_____

_____

_____

How long had you known this person before you realized the friendship wasn't right for you? Was it an easy decision to make or was it difficult? What was the easiest part? What was the most difficult?

?

_____

_____

_____

_____

_____

Did you make the decision alone, or did your friends or parents encourage you to "let go"? What did someone else do that was helpful to you in "letting go"?

_____

_____

_____

_____

How did the other person know you were moving on? Did you tell the person, or did your friends, or did he or she just know you were not committed to being friends any longer?

_____

_____

_____

_____

How did he or she feel about your desire to "move on"? What did he or she say?

_____

_____

_____

_____

How do you feel about your decision? How do you feel about yourself for having made the decision?

_____

_____

_____

_____

This heart, longing for you,
breaks into a thousand pieces—
I wouldn't lose one.

—SHIKIBU

What do you think this quote means?

_____

_____

_____

_____

Taste-Berry Decisions:
Loving Someone Special

I love you because I know you so well; I love you
in spite of knowing you so well!

—*Taste Berries for Teens*

What do you think this phrase means?

99 _____

_____ 99

Do you love anyone "in spite of knowing you so well"? Who?
Why do you love that person?

_____

_____

_____

_____

Does anyone love you "in spite of knowing you so well"? Who?
How do you know?

_____

_____

_____

_____

Taste-Berry Bonds: Expressions of Love

Nothing can match the treasure
of common memories, of trials endured together,
of quarrels and reconciliations and
generous emotions.

—ANTOINE DE SAINT-EXUPÉRY

How does this quote fit your family experience?

_____

_____

_____

_____

One of the first places we can see love is in our homes. Almost every day, the love of our parents and other family members is expressed in many ways—hugs and kisses, gentle reminders and encouragement, as well as their attention to our lives and the things that help us grow up in healthy ways.

List ten of the nicest things the members of your family do for you:

♡ Who: _____

Expression of love: _____

_____

_____

♡ Who: _____

Expression of love: _____

_____

_____

♡ Who: _____

Expression of love: _____

_____

_____

♡ Who: _____

Expression of love: _____

_____

_____

♡ Who: _____

Expression of love: _____

_____

_____

♡ Who: _____

Expression of love: _____

_____

_____

♡ Who: _____

Expression of love: _____

_____

_____

♡ Who: _____

Expression of love: _____

_____

_____

♡ Who: _____

Expression of love: _____

_____

_____

♡ Who: _____

Expression of love: _____

_____

_____

Home is the place where, when you go there,
They have to take you in.

—ROBERT FROST

What else would you like your family members to add to the list of things they do that show you that they love you? List five.

♡ _____

♡ _____

♡ _____

♡ _____

♡ _____

Why do you think they aren't doing these things now?

_____

_____

_____

Name two ways you could communicate your list of needs to your family.

_____

_____

_____

How will you compromise these needs to fit into your family's needs as a whole?

_____

_____

_____

What Do You Do to Show Your Family You Love Them?

List ten of the nicest things you do for the members of your family that shows them you love and appreciate each of them.

♡ Who: _____

Expression of love: _____

_____

_____

♡ Who: _____

Expression of love: _____

_____

_____

♡ Who: _____

Expression of love: _____

_____

_____

♡ Who: _____

Expression of love: _____

_____

_____

♡ Who: _____

Expression of love: _____

_____

_____

♡ Who: _____

Expression of love: _____

_____

_____

♡ Who: _____

Expression of love: _____

_____

_____

♡ Who: _____

Expression of love: _____

_____

_____

♡ Who: _____

Expression of love: _____

_____

_____

♡ Who: _____

Expression of love: _____

_____

_____

_____

_____

_____

If you could add five more things to your list, what would they be?

♡ _____

♡ _____

♡ _____

♡ _____

♡ _____

All a parent can give a child
is roots and wings.

—PROVERB

Taste-Berry Actions: Loving Your Family

Why aren't you doing these things now?

?
_____

_____

_____

_____

_____

How do you think it will make your family feel when you start doing them?

_____

_____

_____

_____

_____

_____

_____

_____

_____

♡   ♡   ♡   ♡   ♡

Bonds of the Heart: Loving Your Family

Write about an incident your family has been through together that made you feel really close to each other. For example, maybe your parents divorced or you lost a family pet and each of you comforted the other during these times. Maybe it was a time you took a special vacation and everyone had such a good time. What was the circumstance? What happened? What made you come together? In what ways did you come together?

_____

_____

_____

_____

_____

_____

_____

How did the incident cause you to care about the members of your family even more? In what ways are you closer now? How does that make you feel?

_____

_____

_____

_____

_____

When you and your parents aren't seeing eye to eye, how does it make you feel? How does it affect you? For example, does it make you irritable with your friends, teachers and others? Do you get quiet, feel sad and get teary?

_____

_____

_____

_____

_____

_____

How do you express those feelings? For example, do you go to your room and want to be left alone, or do you want to talk about it right away? Do you try to punish your parents by pouting, or do you try to get on their good side by doing nice things, such as taking it upon yourself to vacuum or do some other chore without being asked?

_____

_____

_____

_____

_____

_____

When you and your parents are in a good place, how does it
make you feel? How does it affect you? For example, are you
happier when you are with your friends, teachers and others?

_____

_____

_____

_____

_____

_____

How do you express those feelings? For example, are you more
talkative, sharing more with them about what's going on in your
life? Do you tell them "I love you" and "thank you" more often
than usual?

_____

_____

_____

_____

_____

_____

Love Lessons:
Did Someone You Love Leave?

Snowy Bird

*I was visiting a bird sanctuary, when in the dis-
tance, I spotted a young man with a white bird on his
fingers. As he moved the bird up and down, the bird got into
the spirit of things, lifting his little wings up and down in
perfect rhythm with the man's movements. The man gave
a little signal, and the bird began to swing around the
man's fingers, as if a circus acrobat.*

*Enchanted, I walked closer to see the beautiful white
bird perched on the finger of the attendant. "Marty," his
name badge read.*

"Hi, Marty," I said. "Great bird. What is it?"

*"This is Snowy Bird," Marty replied. "He's an umbrella
cockatoo." The cockatoo was snow white in color, a regal-
looking bird with a high plume of feathers fanning from
the crown of his head. But there was one exception to his
majestic appearance—Snowy Bird had no feathers on his
chest. Jarred by seeing this beautiful and obviously tal-
ented bird with such a raw and featherless chest, I asked
Marty, "What happened? Did he have mites?"*

*Marty shook his head and explained, "No, Snowy Bird
plucks out all the feathers on his chest himself. You see,
two years ago his owners had to move out of the state and
felt they could no longer care for him, so they brought
their bird here. Snowy Bird is heartbroken. He still hasn't*

stopped pining for them. One of the ways he mourns them is to pluck the feathers from his chest."

"And he still hasn't gotten over it?" I asked, feeling for this beautiful little bird with a heartache.

"Apparently not," Marty explained. "Whatever it is that goes on in Snowy Bird's head or heart, he is still missing them."

Love, so important—to all of us. Even to umbrella cockatoos, especially one by the name of Snowy Bird who pines to bring back a love and closeness he once knew.

—Bettie B. Youngs, *Taste Berries for Teens*

Did someone you love ever leave you? Who? Why did that person leave? Does it still hurt?

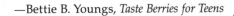

How invisibly it changes color in this world,
the flower of the human heart.

—SHIKIBU

How have you experienced the meaning behind this quote?

_____

_____

_____

_____

Write about a time you were heartbroken. What happened?
Who was involved? What hurt the most, your head or your
heart—or was it difficult to tell?

_____

_____

_____

_____

Did your heart heal or is it still hurting? When your heart is
hurting, how do you comfort it?

_____

_____

_____

_____

Where you used to be there
is a hole in the world.

—EDNA ST. VINCENT MILLAY

Have you ever felt these words? Who left a "hole" in your world? Why?

_____

_____

_____

_____

_____

 "It's the absolute pits to have a huge crush on someone who just sees you as a friend—or worse yet, who doesn't even know you're alive."

—Heather Liston, 16

 "I wanted to be friends with my stepdad, but he didn't want anything to do with me. That hurt."

—Chad Michaels, 15

 "I thought Sara and I were friends for life, but when she started dating MY boyfriend, I knew the friendship was over. Seeing the two of them together was one of the toughest things my heart ever had to deal with."

—Cindi Casass, 17

So many ways for our hearts to be hurt. There are no simple solutions to make the pain go away, and we are left with that age-old adage, "It takes time to heal." The good news is heartache can teach us to be better taste berries, as it makes room in our hearts for compassion, courage, empathy and confidence.

People change and forget to tell us.

—Lillian Hellerman

How have you experienced this quote? What happened? How did this make you feel? How did it turn out in the end?

_____

_____

_____

_____

_____

_____

_____

_____

_____

_____

Love's Lessons: Growing Wiser

Even to think of forgetting
is too painful.

—SHIKIBU

If someone says to you, "don't take it personally," what does that mean to you? Do you think that's possible (to "not take it personally")?

? _____

_____

_____

_____

Have you ever had anyone say things like the following: "Oh, stop wasting your time thinking about him (or her)!" "Just get on with your life!" Or, "Just get over it!" Or, "Don't think about it"? How were these or similar comments either helpful or not at all helpful?

_____

_____

_____

_____

_____

_____

All that we behold is
full of blessings.

—WILLIAM WORDSWORTH

What does this quote mean to you?

_____

_____

_____

_____

What did you learn from going through the hurt? How did your heartbreak help you become wiser? How do you put that wisdom to use?

_____

_____

_____

_____

_____

_____

Loving Yourself Is the Greatest Love of All

Though we like to think we can handle almost anything, our hearts are still sensitive and fragile. So we have to remember to handle them with care. One of the most important things we do in life is learn to love ourselves.

What do you think it means to take care of your heart?

_____

_____

_____

How do you show your love for yourself?

_____

_____

_____

_____

List three things you can do to be good to yourself when your heart is hurting:

♡ _____

♡ _____

♡ _____

Next Time Around: Tomorrow's Taste Berry

When it comes to love, there's always more and there's always next time. The heart is just that way. It's one of the greatest taste berries there is. If a fairy godmother granted you three wishes for having love in your life, what would you ask for?

Dear Fairy Godmother,

Wish # 1: _____

_____

_____

_____

Wish # 2: _____

_____

_____

_____

Wish # 3: _____

_____

_____

_____

Loving the World We Live In

*Without opening your door, you can
open your heart to the world.*

—*TAO TE CHING*

What do you think this quote means?

❧ _____

_____

_____

_____ 🎗

A Message from an Astronaut

From space, the Earth looks like a tiny blue marble lying in an endless black ocean. The Earth appears so small, so fragile, and yet it is our home, one that supports and sustains many forms of life.

As I gaze at our Earth home from space, I am filled with awe for it, and I know that life is sacred. We must each care deeply. Looking out for each other and our Earth home is an act of love. Pay attention to the things going on around you. In the bigger scheme of things, even things that may seem small and insignificant are vital to a healthy Earth and to healthy people. Do your part.

Ironically, it was seeing how small our planet appeared in the very vastness of this universe that filled me with the greatest sense of love for it.

—Steve Smith, veteran of three space flights, over three hundred Earth orbits and five space walks, and, in December 1999, was a crew member of the space shuttle Discovery, who during an eight-hour-long Christmas Eve walk in Space, repaired the Hubble Space Telescope, from *Taste Berries for Teens*

✝ Love asks us to protect all life as sacred. All life is interdependent. When we value this connection we show our love and appreciation for our Mother Earth by protecting our environment.

Three Wishes . . .

You've been given the power to grant Mother Earth three wishes. What do you think Mother Earth would wish for? For example, do you think she would want all her endangered species to be protected, or do you think she would want all her people to be at peace, or would she want all her rivers to be clean again? What are her three greatest wishes and why would she choose each one?

Wish # 1: _____

_____

_____

Wish # 2: _____

_____

_____

Wish # 3: _____

_____

_____

We live in a world that
needs love.

—*Taste Berries for Teens*

PART 4

The Right Stuff: Attitudes for Life Success

Not all birds can fly.
What separates the flyers
from the walkers is the
ability to take off.

—*Carl Sagan*

Taste-Berry Decisions:
A Person of Integrity

I Have to Live with Myself and So . . .

I have to live with myself and so,
I want to be fit for myself to know.
I want to be able as the days go by,
Always to look myself straight in the eye.
I don't want to stand with the setting sun,
And dislike myself for the things I've done.
I can never hide myself from me,
I see what others may never see.
I know what others may never know,
I can never fool myself and so . . .
Whatever happens I want to be,
Self-respecting and conscience free!

—Joy J. Golliver and Ruth Hayes-Arista
I CAN Ignite the Community Spirit

What does "I can never hide myself from me . . . can never fool myself" mean to you?

_____

_____

_____

_____

_____

_____

_____

What does it mean to "*always* look myself straight in the eye"?

_____

_____

_____

_____

_____

_____

_____

Until you make peace with who you are,
you'll never be contented with what you have.

—David McNally

Being a Person of Integrity

*Integrity is being right with yourself—
no secrets, no hidden agenda, no dishonesty, just
"what you see is what you get."*

—TASTE BERRIES FOR TEENS

What does this quote mean to you?

_____

_____

_____

_____

What does having *integrity* mean to you?

_____

_____

_____

Who of all the people you know— including your best friend, your mom or dad, brother or sister, or teachers—do you feel has the most integrity, and why?

_____

_____

_____

How do you know this person has integrity?

_____

_____

_____

Why do you think some people have more integrity than others? What accounts for that?

_____

_____

_____

Always do the right thing. This will gratify some people, and astonish the rest.
—MARK TWAIN

Do you think Mark Twain is right about the notion that doing the right thing will "astonish" some people? Why do you feel this way?

_____

_____

_____

_____

_____

_____

Do you find it hard to "do the right thing" in all situations? Write about a time when you told a lie—such as fibbed about your age to get into a movie or an amusement park for a cheaper price, or drove the family car without first getting permission—and you hoped no one would find out. What was the incident? Who was involved? How did you feel about what you did?

_____

_____

_____

_____

_____

We thought we were
running away from the grownups,
and now we are the grownups.

—Margaret Atwood

How did things turn out? Did you "get away with" your actions? How do you know? Did anyone catch on to your lie? If so, what happened? If no one discovered your lie, how did you feel about what you did?

_____

_____

_____

_____

What do you think is the difference between a *white* lie and a lie?

✝ _____

_____

_____

_____

_____

If someone doesn't agree with you, or doesn't think you did the right thing in a given situation, but you know in your heart that you did the right thing, what would you say to that person?

♥ _____

_____

_____

_____

_____

In thinking, keep to the simple.
In conflict, be fair and
generous.

—*Tao Te Ching*

Taste-Berry Actions: Doing the Right Thing

I Lost a Fast Twenty Bucks

Several months ago while standing in the check-out line at the grocery store, I saw a twenty-dollar bill fall from a lady's purse as she took a check from her wallet. No one even noticed the money float to the floor. I was standing behind her waiting to pay for a bag of M&M's— my regular three o'clock pick-me-up. I leaned over, tucked the cash into my hand and tightened my shoelaces. It was so tempting to pretend the only reason I'd bent down was to tie my shoes. I wanted to go to the fair with my friends on Saturday, and my parents had told me they weren't footing the bill, that I'd have to take care of it myself. I didn't have the money to go to the fair. I looked down at the bill in my hand, thinking that it sure would be handy to have that money! I thought about it—for about three seconds. I knew I had to give her the money back.

The woman was very grateful. Probably as much as I was. As tempting as it was, if I had taken the money, even though no one else might have found out, I would know. Then I'd have to think about how I had stolen it and live with feeling bad about doing it. Even if no one else finds out that you are an honest person, at least you know you are. I know I felt better about myself because I gave the money back to her.

I have integrity—with me.

—Tomoko Ogata, 15, *Taste Berries for Teens*

What would you have done in Tomoko's situation? Why?

_____

_____

_____

_____

Write about an incident where you were really tempted to be dishonest, but thought it through and did what was right—even though you knew that no one else would know about it one way or the other. What happened? Who was involved? How did things turn out?

 _____

_____

_____

_____

_____

_____

_____

♥

You can show all people the way
back to their own nature.

—TAO TE CHING

How did doing the right thing make you feel about yourself? If you didn't do the right thing then, how would you handle it differently today, or would it still be the same?

❓ _____

_____

_____

_____

Who more than anyone else instilled in you the value to do the right thing?

_____

_____

_____

♥

*You have to be honest with everyone—
including yourself. If you can be honest with
yourself, you will automatically
be honest with others.*

—JASON SAMUELS, 16, *TASTE BERRIES FOR TEENS*

Do you agree with this quote? Do you think if you are honest with yourself, you will automatically be honest with others? Why?

_____

_____

_____

_____

Do you trust yourself? How do you know?

_____

_____

_____

_____

Why do you think some people trust themselves more than others do? What accounts for that?

_____

_____

_____

_____

Life would be infinitely easier
if only we could be born at the age of eighty,
and gradually approach eighteen.

—MARK TWAIN

Taste-Berry Actions: Trusting Yourself

Describe an incident that proved you could trust yourself to tell the truth—even when it might have seemed more advantageous to do something different. What happened? Who was involved?

_____

_____

_____

_____

_____

_____

_____

How does being able to count on yourself—to trust yourself—make you feel about yourself?

_____

_____

_____

_____

Nothing in the world is usual today.
This is the first morning.

—Isumi

Do You Trust Yourself?

What is the thing you least trust about yourself? For example, if you have abused drugs in the past but you aren't now and your wish is to stay drug free, and if the friends you hang out with still use, do you find it easy to flirt with the idea of using? Describe an incident that showed you couldn't trust yourself. What happened? What did you do? How did you feel about yourself?

_____

_____

_____

_____

_____

_____

_____

How does not being able to count on yourself—to trust yourself—make you feel about yourself? What are you doing to become a person who has integrity with yourself? What are you doing to develop a greater sense of trust in yourself?

_____

_____

_____

_____

_____

_____

Learning to Trust Yourself

List five things you could do to have *even more* integrity.

EXAMPLE:

<u>I would like to speak up when I hear a friend say something unkind about someone I like—even if I don't know the person very well.</u>

1 _____

_____

2 _____

_____

3 _____

_____

4 _____

_____

5 _____

_____

Taste-Berry Decisions:
Having Good Values

What does "having good values" mean to you?

_____

_____

_____

_____

List nine values that are very important to you—and why.

EXAMPLE:

<u>Value:</u> Keeping my word to my friends.

<u>Why this value is important to me:</u> It makes my friends trust me.

<u>Value:</u> _____

<u>Why this value is important to me:</u> _____

_____

_____

<u>Value:</u> _____

<u>Why this value is important to me:</u> _____

_____

_____

Value: _____

Why this value is important to me: _____

_____

_____

Value: _____

Why this value is important to me: _____

_____

_____

Value: _____

Why this value is important to me: _____

_____

_____

Value: _____

Why this value is important to me: _____

_____

_____

What Do You Value Most?

Value: _____

<u>Why this value is important to me:</u> _____

_____

_____

_____

Value: _____

<u>Why this value is important to me:</u> _____

_____

_____

_____

Value: _____

<u>Why this value is important to me:</u> _____

_____

_____

_____

If someone asked your best friend what you "stood for" (your values), would he or she mention the nine you've listed?

❏ Yes ❏ No

Do you and your friends share the same values? How can you tell?

_____

_____

_____

_____

_____

_____

_____

_____

Do you and your friends talk about what is right and wrong? Why?

_____

_____

_____

_____

_____

_____

_____

_____

Taste-Berry Actions: Walking the Walk

What does the expression "talk your talk, walk your walk" mean to you?

_____

_____

_____

_____

Who is someone you know well who really "talks the talk and walks the walk"?

_____

In what ways does he or she do this?

 _____

_____

_____

_____

*Those who fight for what they want
will always thrill us.*

—Vivien Leigh

Do you "talk your talk and walk your walk"? Describe an incident where it was really tough to "walk your walk" but you did it anyway. What happened? Who was involved?

_____

_____

_____

_____

_____

How did you feel about yourself because you "walked your walk"?

_____

_____

_____

_____

You gain strength, courage and confidence by every experience in which you really stop to look fear in the face.
—ELEANOR ROOSEVELT

Taste-Berry Decisions:
A Person of Action

Waiting for Just the
Right Moment

I really want Madison to be my date for our school prom, which is only four weeks away—but she's a year older than I am, so I've been a little shy about asking her out. My dad knows that I like Madison and asked whether I was going to invite her to the prom. "I'd sure like to," I told him.

"What's stopping you?" he asked. "I'm kind of shy, I guess. And I don't want her to say no." Dad shrugged and said, "She might say no. But maybe she'll say yes."

"I don't want to take the chance that she'll say no," I replied. Dad came back with, "Why don't you ask Madison and let her decide? But she can't make a decision unless you ask her."

He had a point. Even so, I countered, "I just need to wait for the perfect moment." My dad just looked at me and said, "Son, there's no better time than the present. And like I said, she may say yes, and she may say no, but she can't do either until you ask."

I know he's right. I need to get up the courage to ask. And I'd better hurry. If I want Madison as my date to the prom, I'll stand a better chance if I ask her now rather than waiting until it's too late—before someone else does!

—Tom Pierson, 16, *Taste Berries for Teens*

Taking action—or getting motivated—is an important ingredient in "having the right stuff"!

What does "getting motivated" mean to you?

_____

_____

_____

_____

_____

_____

_____

_____

Cheer up!
Remember that the less you have,
the more there is to get.

—CARUSHKA

How Do You Get Motivated?

Describe a time when, like Tom Pierson, you really wanted something—like a date with a certain person, or a particular job, or good enough grades to be accepted into the college of your choice—but the fear that the person might say no to the date, or you might not get the job, or you might not be accepted into the college of your choice made you hesitate, even stall taking action. What were the circumstances? Who was involved?

_____

_____

_____

_____

What made you "get motivated" to do something about it?

_____

_____

_____

Looking back on the incident, how did making the decision to "just do it"—come up with a plan and dig in—make things easier?

_____

_____

_____

How did things turn out? How do you feel about meeting your goals?

_____

_____

_____

_____

Has there ever been a time when you weren't feeling motivated, but you "psyched yourself up" for getting the job done anyway? What was it that you weren't feeling too interested in doing? Who was involved? What happened?

_____

_____

_____

_____

_____

_____

_____

_____

How did you "psych yourself up" to get the job done?

_____

_____

_____

Taste-Berry Actions: "Just Do It!"

Just do it!

—Nike slogan

What do you think this Nike slogan means?

_____

_____

_____

What does it mean to you personally?

_____

_____

_____

How does making the decision to "just do it" make things easier?

_____

_____

_____

Who is the most "motivated" person you know? Why would you say this person is motivated?

_____

_____

_____

Taste-Berry Decisions: "Just Do It!"

The more of life I master, the less of life I fear.

—JENNIFER LEIGH YOUNGS, *TASTE BERRIES FOR TEENS*

What do you think this quote means?

_____

_____

_____

Describe a time when you faced a really big challenge and mastered it. What was the challenge? How did you "master" it?

_____

_____

_____

How did mastering that obstacle help you become a more confident person?

_____

_____

_____

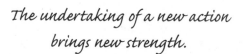

The undertaking of a new action brings new strength.

—EVENIUS

Taste-Berry Actions: Do It Now!

What does it mean to procrastinate?

_____

_____

_____

Are you a procrastinator? _How_ do you know?

_____

_____

_____

_____

Write about an incident where you "procrastinated"—put off doing something you knew you needed to get done, such as getting going on a big assignment or breaking off with a friend you decided was no longer right for you. What were you procrastinating about? What happened? Who was involved? How did things turn out?

_____

_____

_____

_____

_____

How did procrastinating help matters?

_____

_____

_____

_____

How did it hurt them?

_____

_____

_____

_____

What did you learn from the experience?

_____

_____

_____

_____

Someone said that life is a party.
You join in after it's started and leave
before it's finished.

—ELSA MAXWELL

Taste-Berry Decisions: Self-Discipline

Self-discipline leads to
accomplishments—which, in turn,
contributes to a positive self-image, which, in
turn, increases one's self-esteem. One thing leads
to another and another. It's a positive cycle:
One success leads to another success
and yet another.

—*Taste Berries for Teens*

What does this quote mean to you?

Has this—or something similar—ever happened to you: You've been given a big project to do, like a research assignment, one that's not due right away, but soon enough—say, in two to three weeks. The assignment seems overwhelming, and you consider putting off starting on it, but then decide not to put it off, and instead, get started on it. So you make a plan to get busy on it right away. By the time it's due, you've completed it in time—and in style! Because you've had time to do it thoroughly, you turn in a really well-done project.

Describe a time when you made a similar decision. What was the project or task at hand? What did you do about it—what was your "plan of action"?

_____

_____

_____

_____

_____

_____

_____

How did your plan of action lead to a successful outcome?

_____

_____

_____

_____

_____

_____

_____

Success is an "inside" job,
not an "outside" connection.

—LORI GIOVANNONI

Taste-Berry Actions: Being Self-Disciplined

How does self-discipline lead to accomplishment?

_____

_____

_____

Completing a big project—like a research paper that took a lot of work—adds to your sense of achievement. You *can* do it! And, you *did!* How does achievement lead to your self-confidence?

✔ _____

_____

_____

_____

♥

You either have to be first,
best, or different.

—LORETTA LYNN

What do you think this quote means?

_____

_____

_____

Self-Discipline Leads to a
Positive Self-Esteem

For most people, making a decision to get going, to get something accomplished—such as turning in a really well-written project on time—makes them feel *just great* about themselves! Achievement is a wonderful ingredient when it comes to your own sense of self-worth! How does accomplishment lead to a positive self-image?

★ _____

_____

_____

_____

How does a positive self-image contribute to your confidence to do well on future projects?

_____

_____

_____

_____

*How many cares one loses when one decides
not to be something but to be someone.*

—Coco Chanel

Taste-Berry Decisions:
A Person of Determination

In his attempts to create an electric light, Thomas Edison tried and tried and tried before he finally succeeded. After many failed attempts, a critic said to him, "Edison, you should give up. You've failed thousands of times."

"No, I haven't failed thousands of times," Edison retorted. "On the contrary, I have successfully eliminated thousands of ideas that do not work!"

—*Taste Berries for Teens*

What do you think Edison meant when he said, "I have successfully eliminated thousands of ideas that do not work!"

_____

_____

_____

Do you think that we learn as much from what doesn't work as from what *does* work? When was that true for you? Describe a time when you tried something and it didn't turn out as you thought it would, but even so, it was a good learning experience.

_____

_____

_____

Do you think if Edison had given up, someone else would have invented the electric light?

❏ Yes ❏ No

If Edison had given up trying to invent the electric light, and *you* decided to find a way to do it, would you discard what Edison had learned and instead work on your own hunches, or would you look at the progress Edison had made—including reviewing his "failed attempts"? Why would you do this?

?
_____

_____

_____

Write about a "mistake" or "failure" that led you to try again until you succeeded. What was the mistake (or failure)? What did you do? Who was involved? What happened?

_____

_____

_____

_____

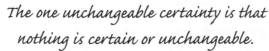

The one unchangeable certainty is that
nothing is certain or unchangeable.

—JOHN F. KENNEDY

Taste-Berry Actions:
Learning from Your Mistakes

Has a mistake or failure ever led to your finding out something important or at least *useful?* What did you find: What was important or at least useful? How did you find this out?

_____

_____

_____

_____

How did things turn out? How did you feel about yourself?

_____

_____

_____

_____

Do you believe in the motto "Don't ever give up"? What does this motto mean to you?

_____

_____

_____

_____

Taste-Berry Decisions: Don't Ever Give Up!

Describe a time when you decided never to give up and, in the end, it paid off. What happened? Who was involved?

?
○ _____

_____

_____

_____

How did things turn out? How did this make you feel about yourself?

_____

_____

_____

_____

What did you learn from this experience?

_____

_____

_____

_____

Whatever your past has been,
you have a spotless future.

—CARUSHKA

Taste-Berry Actions: Determination

Define what "determination" means to you:

_____

_____

_____

Are you a determined person?   ❑ Yes ❑ No

How can you tell?

_____

_____

Would your friends say that you are a determined person?
❑ Yes ❑ No

What example would they give of a time when you really per-
severed—a time when you didn't give up?

_____

_____

_____

_____

_____

_____

_____

Taste-Berry Actions: Perseverance

Describe a time you acted with the greatest determination. Why were you so determined? What was at stake? Who was involved?

☞ _____

_____

_____

_____

_____

_____

_____

_____

How did things turn out? How did you feel about the outcome?

_____

_____

_____

_____

_____

_____

_____

Taste-Berry Decisions: Success

Success is not measured by your victories,
but by your recovery from your failures.

—VIC PREISSER, *TASTE BERRIES FOR TEENS*

What does this quote mean to you?

_____

_____

_____

Describe a time when you "recovered" from a "failure." What happened? How did you know you had "failed"? Who was involved?

_____

_____

_____

_____

How did things turn out? How did you feel about yourself?

_____

_____

_____

Taste-Berry Actions:
Being a Successful Person

Do you think there is a difference between being a successful person and being a success in life?

_____

_____

_____

What does it mean to be a "successful person"?

_____

_____

_____

Do you consider yourself a successful person? Why?

 _____

_____

_____

_____

Success thrives on mistakes.

—LORI GIOVANNONI

How will you know when you are a successful person?

_____

_____

_____

_____

When you meet someone who is "successful," how do you know? How can you tell?

_____

_____

_____

_____

How will others be able to tell that you are a successful person?

_____

_____

_____

_____

The days in my life that stand out most vividly
are the days I've learned something.

—LUCILLE BALL

Taste-Berry Decisions: Be a Hero

I want to be a hero. How about you?
The good news is, everyone is
somebody's hero!

—TASTE BERRIES FOR TEENS

Do you agree with this quote? Do you think it's true that everyone is somebody's hero?

❏ Yes ❏ No

What is a hero?

_____

_____

_____

_____

Whose hero are you? How do you know that person thinks of you as his or her hero?

_____

_____

_____

_____

Why does that person consider you his or her hero?

_____

_____

_____

_____

_____

_____

_____

_____

_____

_____

_____

_____

_____

_____

_____

_____

Life shrinks or expands in proportion
to one's courage.

—ANAÏS NIN

Taste-Berry Actions: Being a Hero

Who more than anyone else is *your* hero (or heroine)?

_____

_____

_____

_____

Write a letter to this person and tell him or her all the ways he or she is a hero or heroine to you.

Dear _____,

Taste-Berry Actions:
Being Someone's Hero

List ten ways *you* are a hero.

EXAMPLE:

I shoot hoops with the eight-year-old across the street whenever I see him alone out playing in his driveway.

1 _____

_____

2 _____

_____

3 _____

_____

4 _____

_____

5 _____

_____

6 ———————————————————————

————————————————————————————————

————————————————————————————————

7 ———————————————————————

————————————————————————————————

————————————————————————————————

8 ———————————————————————

————————————————————————————————

————————————————————————————————

9 ———————————————————————

————————————————————————————————

————————————————————————————————

10 ———————————————————————

————————————————————————————————

————————————————————————————————

It's better to be looked over
than overlooked.

—MAE WEST

Taste-Berry Decisions:
Being a World Hero

Write about what you would do if you were a *World Hero*.
Would you wipe out world hunger and disease or ensure all of
the Earth's creatures are safe? How would you do this—through
some magic invention or formula? What is your greatest vision
or plan for how you would do this? What would be your goal?
Who would you enlist for support and to help? Remember,
there are no limitations when you set out to be a World Hero,
so use your imagination!

_____

_____

_____

_____

_____

_____

_____

_____

*Heroes are just regular folks with one exception:
when someone needs help, they help.*

—*Taste Berries for Teens*

PART 5

Deciding What to Do in Life: Discovering Your Interests, Talents and Direction

*The goal is to
make your joys your job,
your toys your tools.*

—Jennifer Leigh Youngs,
Taste Berries for Teens

Taste-Berry Decisions:
Finding Your Acre of Diamonds

Acre of Diamonds

An Arkansas farmer, tired of not being able to make a good living on his farm, sold it to a man who had very little money, and went off to seek his fortune elsewhere. Several years passed and still he had not found the fortune he sought. Tired, and now broke, he returned to the community of the farmstead he sold. One day, he drove by the farm he once owned—the one on which he could not make a living. To his surprise and amazement, the farmhouse had been torn down and a mansion now stood in its place. Several new buildings, including a large barn, a huge machine shed and a grain dryer and storage unit, had been erected. Rows of trees and shrubs had been planted. Beautiful lawns adorned the meticulously groomed grounds. The place had changed so much that he could hardly believe it was the same farm. He decided to stop and have a talk with the new owner. "Look at all you've done," he remarked, clearly bewildered by what he saw. "How on earth did you accomplish all this? You barely had enough money to buy the farm from me. How did you get so rich?"

The new owner smiled and said, "I owe it all to you. There were diamonds on this property, acres and acres of diamonds!"

> *"Diamonds!" scoffed the previous owner. "I knew every inch of this land, and there were no diamonds here."*
>
> *"On the contrary," responded the new owner as he pulled a lump of what looked like an oily piece of quartz from his pocket. "I carry around this small nugget as a good luck charm."*
>
> *The farmer was amazed. "That's a diamond? I remember seeing a lot of those all over this land, so many that I was frustrated thinking what rotten luck it was to have owned a land filled with hard rock formations—so many that it made plowing and planting difficult!"*
>
> *"Well, it's obvious you don't recognize a diamond when you see one," commented the new owner. "Diamonds in their unpolished form look like lumps of coal."*
>
> —Taste Berries for Teens

Finding your acre of diamonds—discovering what interests you—is an important first step in deciding what you'd like to do as a career.

Do you know what you want to do as a career?   ❏ Yes ❏ No

This is a truth:
Whatever you love, you are.

—RUMI

Taste-Berry Actions:
Looking for *Your* Acre of Diamonds

What do you think it means to find your "acre of diamonds"?

◆ _____

_____

_____

_____

_____

Discovering what interests you can help point you in the direction of what kind of a career you'd like. Maybe you already know exactly what you want to do as a career, or maybe you haven't even given it much thought. Probably you have some friends who know what they want to do when they get out of high school and other friends who don't have a clue. And probably you know those who felt very sure of what it is they wanted to do but then decided against it, and now have no idea.

Finding your acre of diamonds—the search for your interests and talents—is one of the big quests of the teen years. It's just one more of the many important things teens are "supposed" to be thinking about and working through. So even if you have friends who know exactly what they will do the minute they graduate from high school and you don't, or if you think you kinda-sorta know but aren't certain, don't get discouraged.

The important thing is to search for your acre of diamonds. Doing the work that you love to do, having a job that you really enjoy getting up and going to, is a big part of being happy in life. Remember the goal: *to make your joys your job!*

What do you think it means to "make your joys your job"?

_____

_____

_____

_____

_____

_____

_____

Work banishes those three great evils: boredom, vice and poverty.

—Voltaire

Your Scavenger Hunt:
Searching for Clues

The farmer sold his land, certain there was nothing of value on it. Many teens feel the same way, sure they have no special talents they can turn into a job or career. How about you? Have you discovered your "acre of diamonds," or are you still searching?

◆ _____

_____

_____

_____

_____

If you already know your career goal, what is it? How did you discover it? Why do you know it's right for you?

◆ _____

_____

_____

_____

_____

_____

_____

_____

_____

One does not discover new lands
without consenting to lose sight of the
shore for a very long time.
—ANDRÉ GIDE

Have you ever been on a scavenger hunt, a game where you're given a clue, one that leads to the next clue and then the next, and the next, and then, the prize? Discovering what interests you is like that; one thing leads to another and then another. Consider this unit a scavenger hunt, one where you can find your acre of diamonds!

Ready, set, let's go! Here's your first clue . . .

Clue #1 to a Job You'll Enjoy:
Your Personality

A Pain in the Butt

In his acceptance speech for winning an Academy Award for his performance in a motion picture, Robin Williams, the Oscar-winner, thanked a number of people, including some high school teachers. "Some of my teachers thought I was 'a pain in the butt,'" he laughed, referring to himself as a jokester, a funny-bone who could always see the humor in things as a teenager. And then, clutching his Oscar and growing serious, one of America's most beloved comics remarked, "But one special teacher said to me, 'I hope you'll channel that talent. You'd make a good public speaker!'"

—Taste Berries for Teens

Most all of the world knows or has heard of actor and comedian Robin Williams, a man who has certainly succeeded at making his joys his job. If Robin was asked to identify some of his personality traits, probably he would list things like: "I love to be with people; I love to be funny; I love to be outrageous— nothing conservative for me! I love to make people laugh; I love to observe and study people, to see what makes them tick; put me in front of a computer and I'd shriek, 'Get me outta here!'" Stuff like that.

Part of finding your acre of diamonds is recognizing the traits
that make you you. These personality traits are your assets. A
job or career that lets you be you is sure to be more fun than
choosing a job that doesn't fit your personality. If you love
being with people, for example, you probably won't enjoy a
job where you work mainly with machines and have little contact with people.

In each of the following sets of personality traits, which one of
the two best describes you?

_____ I'm quiet and reserved.

_____ I'm outgoing.

_____ I really like to be with a lot of people, even large groups
or a crowd.

_____ I prefer to be alone or in small groups.

_____ I'm a high-energy person.

_____ I'm laid back.

_____ I love animals and have pets.

_____ I don't particularly like to be around animals.

_____ I much prefer indoor activities over outdoor activities.

_____ I prefer outdoor activities over indoor activities.

_____ I'm a good listener, sympathetic and compassionate to the needs of others.

_____ I'm not particularly good at people skills; I prefer working on my computer (or any other solitary activity).

_____ I'm disciplined, and a self-starter.

_____ I'm spontaneous and prefer just going with the flow.

_____ I love being a team player.

_____ I have an entrepreneurial spirit and prefer working by myself.

_____ I love to dress in the latest fashion, the most recent "in" color.

_____ I prefer clothes that are understated and comfortable.

_____ In my spare time, I prefer to have some time to myself, to be by myself.

_____ In my spare time, I prefer to be with friends, doing things socially.

_____ When it comes to sports, I prefer to be a spectator.

_____ When it comes to sports, I prefer playing to watching.

_____ I like to dress up.

_____ I like casual clothes.

____ I like to write about things.

____ I like to read about things.

____ I like to be a leader, to be in charge.

____ I prefer helping out, as opposed to being in charge.

____ I like working with my hands, actually creating or repairing things.

____ I'm an "idea person," and would rather design things in my head and leave working out the details to someone else.

It's a wonderful thing to be able to make a living from just being yourself. List four other personality traits you can add that uniquely describe your personality.

1 _____

_____

2 _____

_____

3 _____

_____

Your personality traits are an important first clue to knowing yourself so you can uncover the kind of work for which you are best suited. For example, if you don't like to be outdoors, it is unlikely you will want to apply to be a firefighter or a conservationist. If you love being outdoors, and if you love nature and working with animals, then you may want to consider work that allows you to do that, and pass up being a psychologist or a social worker, or someone who sits in an office all day working with facts and figures on the computer.

If, on the other hand, you really like to work with people, especially if helping people work through problems is your strong point, then you probably wouldn't want to consider being a veterinarian—unless of course, you work primarily in the front office, talking and interacting with the pet owners.

You'll be much happier doing the kind of work that allows your personality traits to shine, just as Robin Williams's shine in his work!

Ability is the international invitation of power into your life.

—LORI GIOVANNONI

Taste-Berry Actions:
Understanding Your Personality

How fortunate Robin's teacher took notice of his personality and saw great possibility in all the things that
made Robin "Robin." How fortunate she then encour-
aged him to recognize these traits and to consider them
strengths, and coached him to do something with
them. It was to be the start of something very special.
As his Academy Award confirms, the "pain in the butt"
found a way to fashion his personality into a very brilliant diamond!

Who else can help you identify personality traits that might be
helpful in sorting out what sorts of jobs you might like? Ask five
people to give you three words that best describe you. Write
down what they said about you.

◆ _____, my favorite teacher, said
he/she would describe me as a person who: _____

_____

◆ My father said he would describe me as a person who:

_____

◆ My mother said she would describe me as a person who:

_____

_____, my best friend, said he/she would describe me as a person who: _____

_____

 _____, (name of friend/coach/?) said he/she would describe me as a person who: _____

_____

Be bold and go forth
Like it was meant to be,
Your dreams are the gifts
That will set you free.

—Michael Dooley

Clue #2 to a Job You'll Enjoy:
Your Aptitudes

Kevin Got "Lucky"

I found a cat who had been injured and my mother let me take it to the vet and then bring it home.
I knew the cat was in a whole lot of pain. Inside, I just felt this pain for her—almost like I felt it with her. I wanted to make it go away. . . . For some reason, tears came to my eyes. Here I was sitting on my bed, stroking this cat that belonged to someone else and crying. I had never seen the cat before. I didn't understand these feelings. At first, I thought maybe the tears were for the cat who was hurt and lying here without her owner's soothing voice. But then it dawned on me that maybe my feelings were about me. Most of the time I felt bored with everything and everyone around me. I often had this lost, kind of out-of-place feeling inside . . . like I never fit in or had a place where I felt comfortable.
The weirdest—actually not so weird as interesting— feelings came over me. Instantly the idea that I wanted to be a veterinarian came to life in me. Then, an assortment of feelings rushed into my mind. Immediately, I realized— I knew for sure—that I was most happy when I was with animals. But not just in their presence, like when I was horseback riding or at the zoo, but rather, when I was help- ing them, like all the times I had rescued a wounded or sick dog or cat or bird. Whether they were lost, hurt or simply hungry, I always took them in and helped them on their

way. There was this recognition of a lot of feelings, and these feelings took on meaning. I realized that what I was doing was important and that what I did made a difference. I felt honorable and like I had a greater purpose when I was caring for animals.

This incident helped me understand, in a big way, what it was that captured my attention most, where I fit and what made me feel most satisfied. I decided that I was going to be a vet. It was very freeing! Suddenly, I had the urge to get busy. I wanted to find a newspaper to see if there were any part-time jobs in an animal clinic, or maybe even in a pet store. I began wondering if I was smart enough to be a veterinarian, and if it was too late to get better grades in school in order to get into a college. I found myself wondering how long it would take me to become a vet, even where I would go to school, where I would practice.

It was such an energizing feeling. All of a sudden, I was on track. Life mattered, I had things to do. I was important after all. Dreams flooded my mind and filled my head with visions. I saw myself in college, I saw myself in a small practice with other vets, then in a practice of my own and then in an animal hospital that I had built.

—Kevin Tulane, 17, adapted from *Gifts of the Heart*

Wow! Did Kevin get lucky or what! Are you as "lucky" as Kevin?
❏ Yes ❏ No

Taste-Berry Decisions:
Understanding Your Aptitudes

Kevin had a special knack for sensing the needs of wounded animals. It was his strength, something he had a great interest in. When he realized how special and important this was to him, he knew he wanted to make it his life work.

Is there something in particular that holds your attention—something you could see yourself doing? Finding those things for which you have a natural curiosity and attraction is an important second step in deciding what you'd like to do as a career. One way to tell is by taking note of those things that come easily for you.

Our strengths—the areas in which we learn most easily—are different for most of us. Perhaps your friend just has a talent for picking up the latest dance steps within moments of being shown, while you have to really work at it, and even then, you find yourself talking your way through the latest tune. Another friend seems to have a real talent for remembering things she sees but is not as good at remembering things she hears.

This is because we each have different aptitudes. In fact, Harvard psychologist, Professor Howard Gardner, has discovered seven different and distinct types of intelligence. But here's the catch: Rarely, if ever, does anyone have an aptitude in more than two or three of these seven. The trick, of course, is to find which two or three are easy for you.

Here's even better news! You can easily decide which ones you are best at. Read all seven, and then go back and decide which is your strongest point, then the second best, and then your third and so on, all the way through to the ones you are simply not at all good at.

◆ Linguistic Intelligence. This is your ability to read and write, to use words well, like writers, speakers and politicians. People who are linguistically intelligent are systematic, enjoy patterns and order, and have good memories for trivia and word games.

◆ Logical or Mathematical Intelligence. This is your ability to reason or calculate, to be precise—such as is needed to be a good scientist, mathematician or lawyer. People with logical intelligence are good at deductive thinking, using computers and problem solving.

◆ Musical Intelligence. Although you might classify musical ability as a "gift," in fact it is an aptitude, an intelligence. Composers, conductors, musicians, clergymen and spiritual healers rate high in musical intelligence. This is your ability to find it easy to learn dates and to memorize. You also like to do things set to music, whether working or relaxing.

◆ Spatial or Visual Intelligence. This is your ability to remember things in picture forms—such as maps, charts and graphs. You like to see the whole picture all at once rather than learning in bits and pieces, and you use mental images and metaphors for learning. Architects, sculptors and pilots test high in this area.

◆ Kinesthetic or Physical Intelligence. This is your ability to learn by doing and touching. People with physical intelligence have good control over their bodies, like to participate in sports, dance, and anything that requires movements, such as is true for athletes, dancers, gymnasts and surgeons.

◆ Interpersonal or People Intelligence. This is your ability to relate well to others and to understand their feelings. You love to join groups, are very social, a good communicator, do well in activities that require partners or teamwork. Salespeople, negotiators, teachers and coaches rate high in interpersonal skills.

◆ Intrapersonal or Intuitive Intelligence. This is your ability to tap into information stored in the subconscious mind (often called intuition). You are sensitive, self-motivated, understand yourself well, and like to be independent and to take control of your own learning. Philosophers, mystics and counselors show this type of intelligence.

Is this information cool to know, or what! Imagine knowing yourself so well!

Keep in mind that no particular one of these seven is better than the others. All are good—all can indicate areas of talent and aptitude. You may have more than one kind of intelligence; in fact, most of us have strengths in at least two to three areas.

Since most of us find enjoyment in doing things easily and well, this is helpful information, yet another clue to piecing together the job or career you'll enjoy. For example, if you are not at all musically inclined, you may not want to take the time to learn a musical instrument. However, if you love to play both the guitar and the flute, and learning to play them "just seemed to come naturally" to you, then you can be assured the field of music will be an easy one for you to pick up—just as surely as having a talent for reading maps and drawing them to scale could mean a career in the field of architecture might be just perfect for you.

You can start to improve and build on your aptitudes today—which can help you in the future! List your first, second and third areas.

1 _____

_____

_____

2 _____

_____

_____

3 _____

_____

_____

Destiny grants our wishes,
but in its own way, in order to give us
something beyond our wishes.

—GOETHE

Taste-Berry Actions:
Using Your Aptitudes to Find a Career

Is this pretty much what you knew all along? In looking over your first and second aptitudes, and when thinking about those things that come naturally to you, does it all make sense to you now? How did you know you were good in these areas? How long have you known this?

⭐ _____

_____

_____

_____

_____

_____

_____

❤

*Take what you can use and
let the rest go by.*

—KEN KESEY

Now think about your areas of intelligence more closely and examine them for ways you could turn them into a job or career for the future.

EXAMPLE:

First Aptitude: **Musical Intelligence.**
How I could use it: I love music and can play several instruments, including the guitar. I could be in a rock band; I could play studio music backup; I could teach music.

Second Aptitude: **Interpersonal Skills.**
How I could use it: I like people, so I could work in job that gave me direct contact with them—like selling, teaching or counseling.

First Aptitude: **Logical/Mathematical Intelligence.**
How I could use it: I'm good with computers, so I could work in the field of computer technology, even design Web sites.

Second Aptitude: **Spatial/Visual Intelligence.**
How I could use it: I'm good at drawing. I could do graphic design.

What are your top two intelligences and how can you use each of them in a career?

First Aptitude: _____

_____

How I could use it: _____

_____

_____

_____

Second Aptitude: _____

_____

<u>How I could use it:</u> _____

_____

_____

_____

Who could you ask to see what they have to say about your aptitudes? Ask three people whose opinions you trust what they think you'd be good at in a career. Also ask them *why* they think you'd be good at it.

1. Who: _____

What the person said: _____

_____

_____

2. Who: _____

What the person said: _____

_____

_____

3. Who: _____

What the person said: _____

_____

_____

Clue #3 to Finding a Job You'll Enjoy: Your Hobbies

"Mr. Fix It"

My brother couldn't afford a car, so when my uncle bought a new car, he offered my brother his old one—but it needed a lot of repairs. My brother took a shop class to learn how to fix it. He loved the class and now he spends hours under the hood of a car. When he's working on a car, nothing else matters. He can spend hours and hours just tinkering around under the hood.

While the rest of the kids are hanging out in the arcade, not my brother! He's repairing someone's car, or tinkering with his own. There isn't a car he can't get up and running. It's become something he's really good at. All the other guys at school ask my brother for help with their cars, and even my dad trusts him to work on his. The shop teacher saw how much my brother loves to work on cars, and, knowing that he is really good at it, asked him if he'd like a part-time job working in the school's auto repair shop—which he said yes to. I think my brother will probably work on cars for a living. The shop teacher convinced my brother that he should take other classes that would teach him how to run a successful business, like an auto repair shop. I have no doubt that one day he'll have his own auto shop, and all because of his tinkering with cars!

—Mark Knolls, 15, *Taste Berries for Teens*

The goal is to find out what you love to do—whether it's because you're great at it, or it gives you a sense of purpose, or you just think it's fun. Usually, when you find it, it will involve all of these.

While you may think of your hobbies as "just for fun," a careful look at them is an important next step in deciding what you'd like to do as a career. Obviously Mark's brother loves his hobby of fixing cars—so much so, that he loses all track of time when he's doing it.

Think about your three most favorite hobbies. List them in order of how much you enjoy them.

◆ _____

_____

_____

◆ _____

_____

_____

◆ _____

_____

_____

Taste-Berry Decisions: Discovering Your Hobbies

Look closely at your hobbies—you could very well be looking at your acre of diamonds! Think about those times when something you're doing captures your attention to the point that you lose all sense of time—and time just seems to fly by. What are you doing? How long have you had this particular interest?

◆ _____

_____

_____

_____

_____

_____

_____

How do you judge that "time flies by" when you are involved in this activity?

? _____

_____

_____

_____

_____

Is this hobby something that you do alone, or are others involved? For example, is it a team sport or are you cycling alone? Are you sharing information while trading baseball cards, or are you working silently on your computer? Does the fact that you're alone or interacting with others play a part in your attraction to this hobby?

◆ _____

_____

_____

_____

What is it you enjoy most about your hobby?

◆ _____

_____

_____

How can you use your hobby as a way to earn a living, one that could lead to a career? What career could relate to it? How do you know?

◆ _____

_____

_____

_____

_____

Your hobby is a great source of direction toward a career you'll love. Not only does it show you areas of interests, but it also gives you an idea of the skills you enjoy using—skills that can be used in different careers, as well.

Have you ever been in a baseball card shop? When you talk to the owner, you'll usually find he or she is an avid collector whose business started out as a hobby. Talk to someone who has made your hobby his or her life work, such as a photography buff who now owns a camera shop or frame shop. See if you can find someone who shares your interest(s). This could be someone such as the baseball card shop owner if you collect baseball cards, a professional athlete if your hobby is playing sports, or an artisan if you're into crafts. Ask him or her all about it. How did the person get started? What career opportunities does the hobby hold? What skills are related to it, for example, creativity, using your hands, people skills? Write all that you learned from your "hobby expert."

_____

_____

_____

_____

_____

_____

Clue #4 to a Job You'll Enjoy:
Your Part-Time Job!

◆ Sometimes our acre of diamonds is right at our feet—or at the tip of our nose, so to speak. For example, do you have a part-time job or help out one of your parents at work after you get out of school? If so, think about what it is you like and don't like about the work and activities you are assigned.

This information can be used to add yet another clue for where your talents lie. If you dislike stocking shelves but love waiting on customers, it may indicate that you'd like a career working with people. On the other hand, if you just love spending your work hours entering data and dislike having to answer phones, you'd probably be happier in a job where you don't directly deal with people. Kendra Matheson, a high school junior, worked in a clothing store where she discovered she didn't like working the cash register or assisting customers, but absolutely loved window-display design. This led her to pursue a career as an interior designer.

If you have a part-time job (or have had one in the last two years), list all the things you like and dislike about the job. For example, do you like to work with people, but not machines? Do you like to work with machines, but not people? Do you prefer to work alone, or with others in groups? Do you prefer to work outdoors rather than indoors, like when you are sent on deliveries? Remember to try to list *all* the things you like and dislike about the work:

What I like:

◇ _____

◇ _____

◇ _____

◇ _____

◇ _____

◇ _____

◇ _____

◇ _____

◇ _____

◇ _____

◇ _____

What I don't like:

◇ _____

◇ _____

◇ _____

◇ _____

◇ _____

◇ _____

◇ _____

◇ _____

◇ _____

◇ _____

◇ _____

Searching for Clues in Your Part-Time Job

Write about your best day at work ever. What tasks did you do? What were you doing?

_____

_____

_____

_____

_____

_____

_____

Now describe a work situation that helped you clarify that you definitely do not like doing certain sorts of tasks. What are those tasks? How did you learn you don't like them?

_____

_____

_____

_____

_____

_____

_____

Clue #5 to a Job You'll Enjoy:
Looking for Gifts in Disguise!

A Gift in Disguise

I really wanted a certain part in the spring play our high school drama club was putting on. I knew I'd be great in the part because I'd been in plays for the last three years and really like acting. I've even thought about being an actor.

Well, I didn't get the part. The teacher asked each of us to help with the lighting and sound, as well as with other behind-the-scenes roles. At first I was upset at not being chosen for the lead role, especially when I was assigned to the behind-the-scenes work. But then I decided, why not learn all you can about the theater? It might come in handy to know this stuff. Boy, did I find out how true that was! Not only did I learn that I was really good at production and behind-the-scenes work, I also found out I enjoyed it. What I didn't know was that I would enjoy it even more than acting! Now I'm certain that I want to be a film producer. Move over, Steven Spielberg! As it turned out, it was really good that I didn't get chosen for the part. I'm happy that I agreed to work backstage. It was a gift in disguise—because I've discovered my acre of diamonds. So, be open to experiences, and to learning all you can!

—Richard Lewis, 17, *Taste Berries for Teens*

Has anything like this ever happened to you? Write about an incident when you wanted one thing to happen, but something else totally different happened—and you got more than you expected out of it. What happened? Who was involved? What did you discover? Do you think you've found your acre of diamonds?

_____

_____

_____

_____

_____

_____

_____

_____

_____

_____

_____

_____

_____

Taste-Berry Actions:
Looking for Gifts in Disguise

Use this page to journal any unexpected clues you stumble upon each day:

_____

_____

_____

_____

_____

_____

_____

_____

_____

_____

_____

_____

_____

_____

_____

_____

_____

_____

Clue #6 to a Job You'll Enjoy: Asking Others What They Think You'd Be Good At

"Two-Hundred and Fifty-Six!"

Of all the teachers I had, Mr. Swede impressed me the most because I could tell he loved teaching and really liked his students. To me, he seemed to be living his dreams, doing exactly what he wanted to do. Mr. Swede was brilliant—he knew his subject so well. Facts just poured from him, and he knew how to make them interesting to his students. There was something about his love for the subject that made history come alive for me, too.

During our timed midterm essay, we had to write all the facts we could remember about the civil rights movement. I wrote eighteen pages, 256 facts—more than anyone else in the class. After that, as Mr. Swede walked around the room while we were doing our written assignments in class, he would pass my desk and pause to whisper, "Two-hundred and fifty-six, imagine!" as if to remind me of how well I had done—and what I could do. On occasion, he'd say, "Be sure to talk with the counselors about universities!" Other times, he'd say, "You know, you could teach history." I found that so inspiring. Last year, at the end of my junior year in high school, I asked him to sign my yearbook. In it he wrote: "You have great promise. I hope you'll work hard, go to a fine university, and help change the world. If ever you doubt yourself, just remember, 'Two-hundred and fifty-six!'"

I don't know if I'll get accepted to a college, but I am trying. Every few months, I get out my annual and read what he wrote. Mr. Swede's words and his belief in me and my talent remind me that I really do have promise. Whenever I doubt myself, I recall the affirming tone of his voice and his words, "Two-hundred and fifty-six!"

I admire Mr. Swede and value his opinion. If he thinks I'd be a good history teacher, maybe I would be. I've been seriously considering teaching. I think I could be a good teacher!

—Lana Bowman, 17, *Taste Berries for Teens*

Have you ever had a teacher who thought you'd be good at something in particular? Who was the teacher? What did he or she suggest? Do you think the teacher is right about that?

_____

_____

_____

_____

_____

Taste-Berry Actions: Asking Others What They Think Is a Good Career Choice for You

⭐ Just as Mr. Swede helped Lana Bowman feel confident that she could be an educator, you can ask others what they think might be suitable kinds of work and careers for you. Ask five people to give you their opinions on what they think might be a good career choice for you. Be sure to ask for reasons as to why they think this way.

1. _____, my favorite teacher, said he/she thought I might be wise to choose a career in _____

because _____

_____

_____

_____

2. My father said he thought I might be wise to choose a career

in _____

because _____

_____

_____

_____

3. My mother said she thought I might be wise to choose a career in _____

because _____

_____

_____

_____

4. _____, my school counselor, said he/she thought I might be wise to choose a career in _____

because _____

_____

_____

_____

5. _____ (name) said he/she thought I might be wise to choose a career in _____

because _____

_____

_____

_____

Do what you love
Love what you do. And the
World will come to you.
—MICHAEL DOOLEY

Clue #7 to a Job You'll Enjoy:
Observing Others in Their Work

Another way to find your acre of diamonds is to check out how others have unearthed their own! Noticing how others show their interest and passion for their work can really help you see what interests you. Once you have that direction, you can learn more about what tasks different professionals perform and what different positions and career options are available.

List four people you know who are doing work that they love, and what it is they are doing. How do you know each one loves his or her work?

EXAMPLE:

<u>Who:</u> Mr. Swede.

<u>Chosen Work:</u> Teaching history.

<u>How I can tell he loves his job:</u> He's very excited about what he's teaching. He likes his students. You can tell he wants his students to learn what he is teaching; he cares.

◆   Who: _____

Chosen Work: _____

_____

How I can tell he/she loves his or her job: _____

_____

_____

◆   Who: _____

Chosen Work: _____

_____

How I can tell he/she loves his or her job: _____

_____

_____

_____

◆   Who: _____

Chosen Work: _____

_____

How I can tell he/she loves his or her job: _____

_____

_____

_____

◆   Who: _____

Chosen Work: _____

_____

How I can tell he/she loves his or her job: _____

_____

_____

_____

Why is it important to love your job?

_____

_____

_____

_____

_____

_____

What will you do if you get a job and then decide you don't like it?

_____

_____

_____

_____

_____

_____

Clue #8 to a Job You'll Enjoy:
Looking to Your Personal Experiences
and Lessons Learned

Seventeen-year-old single mother Julie Newman found her diamonds when taking her ten-month-old baby daughter to an infant care center at her school. Noticing all the many different kinds of baby toys and mobiles that were used, Julie learned these toys are important for developing the baby's brain and alertness and intelligence. She discovered she wanted to design toys for infants, most especially for a baby's crib, toys that keep them stimulated, alert and learning.

Josh Henderson found his acre of diamonds as the result of his whole world crashing in on him. Drug abuse had made a complete disaster of his life. When Josh made a U-turn, and turned his whole life around, he became interested in using what he'd learned and experienced to help others. Josh wants to be a drug counselor and work with troubled teens; he feels he has something to offer because he's been there. He's enrolled in junior college and is taking courses toward a career doing just that.

Unlikely clues lie all around you. Remember, the farmer who sold his land didn't see any acres of diamonds—but they were right there, hidden in what appeared to him to be nothing more than ugly rocks that made his plowing harder. Yet even hardships and challenges can point you to your diamonds.

Write about an event or circumstance in your life that taught you a lesson, one that you feel is worth sharing with others. What happened? Who was involved? How did what happened affect your life? How did things turn out? What would you like others to know as a result of what you've learned?

How can you use this experience in your future—will you write a book about it or write an article for a magazine, for example? How can you go about teaching others—will you do workshops for youth, parents or the business community? List as many ways as you can think of. If there were others involved in the experience, for example, if you saw a counselor, therapist, physician, probation officer or someone else who helped you get through this experience, you might ask them about how to best use the experience to share it with others, or how to use what you've learned in a job or career. Maybe they had a similar experience and it's why they chose their work!

◇ _____

◇ _____

◇ _____

◇ _____

◇ _____

◇ _____

◇ _____

◇ _____

◇ _____

◇ _____

◇ _____

◇ _____

◇ _____

◇ _____

◇ _____

Clue #9 to a Job You'll Enjoy: Check with Your Friends

Matt Jeffries confessed he was "clueless" as to what his acre of diamonds might be. "I don't have any idea what I want to do after I graduate," sixteen-year-old Matt said. "Sometimes I get really bummed out about it, because it seems like everyone else knows exactly what they want to do, like what college they want to attend—or at least where they want to apply. Some of my friends even know what they want to do for work."

Do you and your friends talk about what you want to do when you graduate?

❏ Yes   ❏ No

List the careers two of your friends are interested in. If you don't know, ask them.

◆   Who: _____

What this person thinks he or she will choose for a career: ____

_____

◆   Who: _____

What this person thinks he or she will choose for a career: ____

_____

Talking Work with Your Friends

Knowing your friends, can you see them in these careers? Why?

_____

_____

_____

Would either of these careers interest you? Why or why not?

_____

_____

_____

Do you think your friends have an idea of what you should do for a career? Have you asked them? What did they say? (If you haven't asked them, do so now.)

_____

_____

_____

What are their reasons for thinking a certain career would be ideal for you? Why do you agree or disagree?

_____

_____

_____

Clue #10 to a Job You'll Enjoy: Looking to Your Dreams for Your Future

Seventeen-year-old Trent Dayton has a passion for the ocean and surfing. Trent said that some people called him a "surf bum" and didn't see him as having big goals or plans for his future. But Trent has a dream: to own his own surf shop and to manufacture his own surfboards. In fact, he's already developed great skill at shaping surfboards and knows all there is to know about what a surfboard shop needs to carry. Add his knowledge and skills to his passion for the ocean and for surfing, and you have a large arrow pointing to the entrance of a diamond mine. It all came to life with his dream.

What is your dream? How long have you had this dream? Who have you told about this dream?

★ _____

_____

_____

_____

_____

_____

Looking to Your Dreams for Your Future

How could your dream point you in the direction of making your joys your job?

➤ _____

_____

_____

_____

_____

There was a time Trent might have described his love of surfing as just an "interest" he had. But now that he's identified his dream, he's better able to decide what further education and training he needs to give wings to his goals.

Can you see yourself in your future? When you think about "your future," how far away is that? What does the term "future" mean to you?

? _____

_____

_____

_____

_____

Clue #11 to a Job You'll Enjoy: Creating a Vision for *Your* Future

A vision sets direction for
thinking and action.

—EDWARD DE BONO

A vision for what you want, your ideal, and where you're headed, is an important part of making a dream come true. It's a vision in your mind's eye of your future.

Picture yourself at twenty-five years old. Where are you living—what city and state?

_____

_____

_____

_____

Are you renting an apartment, or buying a condo or house? What does your home look like? How big is it? Is it small or large? Is it one bedroom, two or three? What is the color of your carpet—or do you have stone or wood flooring? Describe your furniture, the pictures on the walls and your furnishings.

_____

_____

_____

_____

_____

_____

_____

_____

_____

_____

_____

_____

_____

_____

What sort of car are you driving? What is the year, make and model? Are you buying your car, or leasing it?

_____

_____

_____

_____

_____

Taste-Berry Actions:
Creating a Vision for "Future"

What are you doing for work? Did you graduate from college and are you in your first job? Did you go to trade school and have you been in the work force for a couple of years? Are you working for a company (large or small?) or for yourself? Are you paid by the hour or do you have a salary? How much do you earn a year? Do you have a savings account, checking account and credit cards?

_____

_____

_____

_____

_____

Who are your friends? Are they the same faces from junior high and high school, or are they mostly new friends you've made at work and in your personal life, like working out at the gym, shopping and in your leisure-time activities?

_____

_____

_____

_____

_____

Do you work out regularly? Do you belong to your local gym or workout center? How often do you work out? Are you in good shape? Are your friends into fitness?

◈ _____

_____

_____

_____

Do you enjoy cooking at home or do you eat out as often as you can? What sort of restaurants do you go to? What sort of foods do you enjoy when cooking at home? Do you often have friends over for meals? Do they join you in the kitchen and help you cook the meal, or do they expect you to have the meal prepared ahead of time?

★ _____

_____

_____

_____

_____

How do you spend your weekends?

♥ _____

_____

_____

Do you live alone or with a roommate? If you live with someone, how did you meet? What sort of person is he or she? What
does he or she look like; what sort of a job does he or she have;
did that person graduate from college; do the two of you share
the same values? Do you have the same friends? Do you work
out together, buy groceries together, socialize together? Do you
have pets?

_____

_____

_____

_____

_____

_____

Are you single, or married? Describe the person you are dating
(or married to). What does he or she look like? What sort of a
job does he or she have? Did that person graduate from college? Do the two of you plan to have children—and if so, how
many?

_____

_____

_____

_____

_____

Clue #12 to a Job You'll Enjoy: Setting Goals

How do you plan to get from where you are today, to your "future"? Having goals is the key.

A goal is like having a map. If you know the direction you should head, you know where to focus your time and energy. Channeling your efforts in a single direction can keep you on track so that you actually get to your destination. Goals point you in the direction of where you should be spending your time so you can get things accomplished. Write down your goal in each category.

Dear (Goal) Diary,

JOB OR CAREER SATISFACTION: This includes goals for getting a job or for preparing for what you want to do as a career.

Goal: _____

_____

_____

_____

_____

_____

LEARNING AND EDUCATION: What would you like to know more about? What skills do you want to develop? To what formal education do you aspire?

Goal: _____

_____

_____

_____

_____

PERSONAL GROWTH: This includes goals for peace of mind, your search for spiritual meaning, developing your personal strengths (such as discipline or patience) and maintaining your values. Do your career goals align with these goals, too?

Goal: _____

_____

_____

_____

_____

You've removed the roadblock to
success when you've learned the difference
between motion and direction.

—BILL COPELAND

Taste-Berry Actions: Setting Goals

What obstacles stand in your way and can prevent you from achieving your goal? For each goal, ask the following three questions:

1. What obstacles do I need to overcome?
2. What action can I take to overcome those obstacles?
3. Whom will I ask for help, support and assistance in meeting the goal?

EXAMPLE:

Goal: To stay on the honor roll so I can get into a good college.

Obstacles to overcome: I can't get the hang of geometry.

Sometimes I procrastinate and don't get my homework done.

What action I'll take to overcome those obstacles: I'll set aside the first half hour after dinner to study geometry. I'll make a regular, no exceptions, time to do my homework—and I won't take any phone calls until I'm finished.

Whom I will ask for help and support in meeting the goal: I'll ask my brother to tutor me and help me understand geometry.

I'll ask my best friend to encourage me by making sure I've gotten my homework done before we talk on the phone at night.

◆ Goal: _____

Obstacles to overcome: _____

_____

What action I'll take to overcome those obstacles: _____

_____

_____

Whom I will ask for help and support in meeting the goal: ____

_____

◆ Goal: _____

Obstacles to overcome: _____

_____

What action I'll take to overcome those obstacles: _____

_____

_____

Whom I will ask for help and support in meeting the goal: ____

_____

◆ Goal: _____

Obstacles to overcome: _____

_____

What action I'll take to overcome those obstacles: _____

_____

_____

Whom I will ask for help and support in meeting the goal: ____

_____

Taste-Berry Actions:
Achieving Your Goals

I wasn't sure what kind of career I wanted, but I figured at the very least, going to college would give me four more years to get it figured out. So I talked to my guidance counselor who gave me a lot of useful information on how to go about getting into college. He gave me brochures, applications and other information from colleges all over the country. I learned that my school even offered a tour of some major universities in my home state and that colleges are ranked academically, financially and by certain majors— some brochures even describe campus life. That was really helpful. There are even software programs that give brief overviews on hundreds of colleges.

Deciding on a college that's right for you takes a lot of thought and research, but the way I figure it, a good education is worth it.

—Danny Benjamin, 17, *Taste Berries for Teens*

Do you want to go to college?   ❏ Yes ❏ No

If you'd like to go to college but can't afford it, what are your plans to get into college?

_____

_____

_____

_____

How might college be an important step toward choosing a career if you don't already know what career you're interested in?

_____

_____

_____

_____

If you already know what career you want, what kind of degree do you need to follow your dreams and attain that career? How did you find this out? Who was helpful in this discovery?

_____

_____

_____

_____

What colleges offer degrees in the field you hope to enter? How did you find this out? Who helped you discover these colleges?

_____

_____

_____

_____

What are four steps you should take to find the right college for you?

1 _____

_____

_____

2 _____

_____

_____

3 _____

_____

_____

4 _____

_____

_____

Whenever you see a successful person,
someone made a courageous
decision.

—PETER DRUCKER

Clue #13 to a Job You'll Enjoy: Achieving Your Goals

Your goals are stepping stones that move you toward your ultimate dream. These include short-term and long-term goals. Short-term goals are all those things you can do right now that move you toward your dream. Long-term goals include the things you are moving toward and plan to do in the future to move toward your dream, which is your ultimate goal.

EXAMPLE:

<u>Short-Term Goal:</u> Get one of my cartoons in the school newspaper.

<u>Short-Term Action Plan:</u>
1. Take art classes.
2. Follow the work other cartoonists are doing.
3. Keep submitting my cartoons for consideration in the paper.

List three steps it will take—your action plan—to reach your short-term goals that move you toward your long-term career goals:

<u>Short-term goal:</u> _____

_____

1 _____

_____

2 _____

3 _____

EXAMPLE:

Long-Term Goal: I want to be a cartoonist.

Action Plan:
1. Improve my art skills.
2. Get into a good art college.
3. Get published in as many papers as possible.

List three steps it will take—your action plan—to reach the ultimate goal of the career of your dreams. You'll want to list things like what education and training you'll need:

Long-Term goal: _____

_____

1 _____

2 _____

3 _____

Clue #14: Taste-Berry Decisions:
Being a Success

Being a "success in life" means different things to different people. What is your definition of success?

★ _____

_____

_____

_____

How will you know if you "become a success"?

_____

_____

_____

_____

How will being successful make you a different person than you are now? In what ways will you be different?

_____

_____

_____

_____

PART 6

Making a Difference

*Sometimes the
brightest sparks come
from the smallest fires.
There is power in every act of
kindness, however small or grand.*

—Deborah Spaide, founder, Kids Care Clubs

Taste-Berry Decisions: Making a Difference

Saving a Lizard

I think that every little thing we do in life makes a difference. This morning before I left for school I rescued a lizard from the paws of my cat. I know it made a difference. That lizard may eat an insect that would have eaten a bud on a flower waiting to bloom, one that a bee would have depended upon for honey, a flower that in turn depends upon the bee to spread its pollen. All species of animals and plants and humans on Earth are linked together. As a matter of fact, every living thing is connected to each other in one way or another.

And everything we do, good or bad, affects all of us, including the condition of the universe and all its planets.

Rescuing a lizard was one way for me to do my part. At the very least, I know it made a difference to the lizard. And I also know the lizard is connected in the chain of things, so I made a difference on a bigger level as well. We each have a special role in keeping the world going.

—Brian Lumke, 13, *Taste Berries for Teens*

Do you think Brian's actions make as big a difference as he thinks they do? Why do you feel this way?

_____

_____

_____

_____

_____

_____

_____

What does it mean to "make a difference"?

_____

_____

_____

_____

_____

_____

_____

How Do You
Make a Difference?

Who do you think makes the *most difference* in the entire world?

♥ _____

_____

_____

_____

How does this person make a difference? What does he or she do that makes you think so?

_____

_____

_____

_____

Do you think this person makes a bigger difference than, say, Brian Lumke, who rescued a lizard from the jaws of his cat? Why do you think so?

_____

_____

_____

_____

> *Making a difference can begin with the smallest things—such as being thoughtful and courteous. Probably we don't always know when the little things we do make a difference to others, but that doesn't make them any less important.*
>
> —*Taste Berries for Teens*

What does this quote mean to you?

_____

_____

_____

_____

What do you think is more important:

❏ making a difference in your family?

❏ making a difference within your circle of friends?

❏ making a difference in your community?

❏ making a difference to someone in great need in another part of the world?

Why do you feel this way?

_____

_____

_____

Where do you feel you make the most difference:

❏ in your family?

❏ within your circle of friends?

❏ in your community?

❏ to someone in great need in another part of the world?

Do you think some people make a bigger difference than others? Why or why not?

---

*It is good to have an end
to journey towards; but it is the journey
that matters, in the end.*

—URSULA LE GUIN

Taste-Berry Actions: Making a Difference

Being a taste berry might change someone else's life—maybe even your own. "What goes around, comes around," is a popular phrase used to describe the natural principle of reaping what you sow, getting what you give—what you put out comes back to you. This is never more true than when it comes to giving and helping others.

Write about a time when you were helpful or kind and it "came back to you." What was the situation or circumstance? Who were you helping or showing kindness to? Why did this person need help?

_____

_____

_____

_____

_____

How did your gesture "come back to you"? Who was kind to you? How was this person kind to you?

_____

_____

_____

_____

_____

_____

_____

_____

_____

How did it feel when the kindness was returned? How did it affect the way you felt about others and looked at the whole world?

_____

_____

_____

_____

_____

_____

_____

_____

_____

Taste-Berry Decisions: Sharing with Others

"His" Bracelet

I had gone with a group of seven teens from our church to spend a day with children in a shelter for abused and abandoned kids. While most of the children were glad to see us, some just stood looking, as though they were suspicious. One little boy in particular caught my attention. His hands jammed in his pockets, the little guy just glared at us, his eyes filled with mistrust. It was disquieting.

We'd come to play with the children, to be their "big brothers" for the day. Right after lunch, we did a sing-along. I sat in the back to encourage the boys there to sing along. As I looked over at the group, Charlie, the boy I'd noticed glaring at us when we arrived, was looking in my direction, staring at the bracelet I wore. When I had first seen it in a store window several weeks before, I loved it and knew I had to have it. I wore it all the time. I watched Charlie for a moment, and when he glanced at me, I smiled at him. He quickly turned his eyes from mine. Several minutes later, I noticed Charlie once again just staring at my bracelet. When Charlie realized I was looking at him, this time, he pointed at the bracelet—and smiled! I smiled back, and went over and sat beside him. Though a little nervous, Charlie continued to smile, and then, slowly reached over—watching my eyes—and gently touched my bracelet. Thinking it would be a nice gesture to let him

*try it on, I took the bracelet off and placed it on his wrist.
You should have seen how large his eyes became. A smile
lit up his whole face. I decided I'd let him wear the bracelet
for a while. Charlie sat beside me for the remainder of the
songs, holding my hand and leaning his head against my
arm! As soon as the songs were over, Charlie jumped up
and ran over to show the other children the bracelet. He
pointed in my direction, and all heads turned to look in my
direction, then back at the bracelet. Each of the boys took
turns touching the bracelet, murmuring their approval.
With a look of pride, Charlie said, "He gave it to me!"*

*When I saw how special the bracelet was to him—even
though I loved the bracelet and wanted it for myself—I
said, "It's for you. It's your bracelet." Charlie smiled and
tears welled up in his eyes. "For me," he confirmed. I
thought about Charlie all the way home. In the morning,
he had been scared and mistrusting, by the afternoon he
was holding my hand as we did a sing-along. It was such
a big change. And the bracelet—it meant so much to him
to have someone give him something that he obviously
liked so much. I went there to volunteer my time with the
boys. That was to be the gift I was giving. But it was giving Charlie my prized bracelet that was the best gift
of all. To him. And to me.*

—Steve Hand, 16, *Taste Berries for Teens*

Do you think it was wise of Steve to give up his favorite bracelet? Why do you feel this way?

_____

_____

_____

_____

_____

_____

What would you have done in Steve's place? Why would you make that decision?

_____

_____

_____

_____

_____

_____

_____

_____

Taste-Berry Actions: Sharing with Others

Describe a time when you were given a chance to share in a similar way Steve was able to share with Charlie. What was the situation? Who was the person you were able to share with? What did you share? How did sharing make you feel?

_____

_____

_____

_____

_____

_____

_____

_____

_____

_____

What was it about the experience that was memorable and made the expression "It's more fun to give than to receive" ring true?

_____

_____

_____

_____

Taste-Berry Decisions:
Giving to Others

Describe a time when you gave a gift to someone. What was the gift you gave? Who did you give it to? Why did you give this person a gift?

_____

_____

_____

_____

How did the other person feel about receiving a gift from you? How do you know this?

_____

_____

_____

_____

How did "giving" make you feel? For example, did seeing that person's happiness make your own even more complete?

_____

_____

_____

_____

Taste-Berry Decisions: Serving Others

It is our obligation—as much as it is our honor—to help others see their lives in the most positive light.

—BETTIE B. YOUNGS, *TASTE-BERRY TALES*

What does this quote mean to you?

_____

_____

_____

_____

_____

_____

_____

_____

_____

Kindness, service and doing our part to make a difference in the world are more than just "quick heart warmers," they are also our responsibility, our obligation and our honor in being of service to others. Since we are a global family, we are all responsible for each other, as well as for the planet we share.

Write about a time when you agreed to volunteer or to do something for others. What were you asked to do? What was your role or responsibility? Were you working with children or adults, or were you assisting with animals or some sort of clean-up duties? How much time was involved—was it a one-time event, or was it a commitment for a week, a month or a year? Did you work alone or in a group?

_____

_____

_____

_____

_____

_____

_____

_____

_____

_____

_____

_____

Taste-Berry Actions: Serving Others

What was the experience like? Did you enjoy it, or not particularly? Was it what you expected—or not at all? Explain.

?
_____

_____

_____

_____

_____

What did you learn from the experience? For example, did you decide never to volunteer again, or did you decide to make volunteering a regular part of your life? Did you decide you'd like to volunteer, but not to do that kind of work again? Or, did the experience of working in a particular setting or with a particular group—such as seniors, children or animals—open you to ideas of what you might want to do for a living?

_____

_____

_____

_____

_____

_____

_____

In what way was the experience an "honor"?

_____

_____

_____

_____

How did your volunteering—helping others—make a differ-ence to those you served? How do you know this to be true?

_____

_____

_____

_____

How did your volunteering make a difference in the world? How do you know?

_____

_____

_____

_____

Taste-Berry Decisions:
Assisting Others

Rabbi Wayne Dosick's home recently burned to the ground in a wildfire. It wasn't just family, friends and the Red Cross who came to his family's aid, but also a group of teens in his neighborhood. The teens took up a collection of their own money and raised three hundred dollars, then went to the local hardware store to buy tools their neighbors would need to dig through the ashes. When the manager of the store heard what they were doing, he matched their three hundred dollars!

As news of what they were doing spread through the store, other customers began donating money, and another five hundred dollars was raised. The next day, all of the kids piled into one of the store's trucks and drove through the neighborhood handing out all the tools to their neighbors—over eleven hundred dollars in shovels, rakes, work gloves, wastebaskets and garbage bags.

—Taste Berries for Teens

Some people seem as if they are always open to helping others—as if they've made the decision to be helpful and doing so just comes naturally for them, like the teens who lived in Rabbi Wayne Dosick's neighborhood.

Do you have friends like that? Name five friends who are always helping others:

1 _____

2 _____

3 _____

4 _____

5 _____

*There's more to life than
increasing its speed.*

—GANDHI

Taste-Berry Actions:
Assisting Others

Helping is an attitude, more than anything else—an attitude of compassion and willingness to assist. If you are open to helping others, usually you'll find the opportunity right at the tip of your nose.

—*Taste Berries for Teens*

What does this quote mean to you?

_____

_____

_____

_____

Write about a time when you ended up doing something for somebody on the spur of the moment because you were open to being helpful and saw an opportunity. What was the situation? What did you do to help? Who needed your assistance?

_____

_____

_____

_____

_____

_____

_____

_____

_____

How did being able to help make you feel about yourself? How did it make you feel about the person you were able to help— for example, did you make a new friend?

_____

_____

_____

_____

_____

_____

_____

_____

_____

_____

Taste-Berry Decisions:
Tolerance for Others

*All of us—no matter how old or how young—
need others to show us patience and tolerance.*

—AUTHORS, *TASTE BERRIES FOR TEENS*

What does this quote mean to you?

_____

_____

_____

_____

Because it's only natural to think of teenagers as capable and self-sufficient people, it's easy to forget teens still need others to show patience, tolerance and direction. Do you think adults are less tolerant with teens than they are with children and seniors? Describe a time when this was true for you.

_____

_____

_____

_____

_____

Why do teens—just as much as seniors and children—need others to show patience and tolerance toward them?

_____

_____

_____

_____

_____

_____

Name one adult you wish would show more patience and tolerance for you. How would you like them to show more patience and tolerance?

_____

_____

_____

_____

_____

_____

_____

_____

_____

_____

Taste-Berry Decisions:
Speaking Words of Kindness

The smallest acts of kindness—even in the form of a few kind words—can make a difference in the life of someone else. Write about a time someone shared "a few kind words" at a moment you really needed it. What was going on for you at the time that made it so meaningful? Who shared those words with you? Why was that person "there for you"?

_____

_____

_____

_____

_____

_____

_____

_____

Exactly what did the person say to you?

_____

_____

_____

_____

_____

How did what was said make you feel, for example, were his or her words comforting or inspiring? How did this make you feel about the person?

_____

_____

_____

_____

_____

_____

_____

Beauty is more than in the eye of the beholder; it is in the heart of the joyful.

—LORI GIOVANNONI

Taste-Berry Actions:
Speaking Words of Kindness

Write about a time when you shared "a few kind words" when someone else really needed them. Who was the person? What was going on for him or her at the time? Why did you feel this person needed your comfort or encouragement?

_____

_____

_____

_____

_____

_____

_____

_____

_____

What did you say? Did it seem to help? How did you know?

_____

_____

_____

_____

How did you feel about yourself after helping someone through a tough spot?

? _____

_____

_____

_____

How do you think that person felt about you because of what you did?

_____

_____

_____

_____

_____

_____

_____

_____

_____

If you stop to be kind,
you must swerve often from
your path.

—MARY WEBB

Taste-Berry Decisions:
Being Kind and Considerate

Kind words and actions are among the things we "give" that help make the world a "better place." Do you consider yourself a kind and considerate person? How do you know?

_____

_____

_____

_____

List four things you've done that were kind and considerate, and how your actions made the world a better place.

EXAMPLE:

What I did: I asked a new girl at school to sit with me and my friends at lunch.

How this makes the world a better place: By extending my friendship, she may do the same for someone else—and because I invited her to meet with my friends, my friends might do something nice for someone else also. Friendship creates harmony in the world.

What I did: _____

How this makes the world a better place: _____

_____

_____

What I did: _____

How this makes the world a better place: _____

_____

_____

_____

What I did: _____

How this makes the world a better place: _____

_____

_____

_____

What I did: _____

How this makes the world a better place: _____

_____

_____

_____

Taste-Berry Decisions:
See a Need and Fill It

Do all the good you can, by all the means you can,
in all the ways you can, in all the places you can,
at all the times you can, to all the people you can,
as long as you ever can.

—JOHN WESLEY

What does this quote mean to you?

_____

_____

_____

_____

Doing all the good you can—helping others in your community, being of service, making a difference—can be as easy as seeing a need and doing what you can to fill it.

List three needs that you see in your community. What can you do to help fill each of those needs?

EXAMPLE:

Community need: The recreation center needs volunteers.

<u>What I can do to help fill this need:</u> I can volunteer at the recreation center after school to help out with the younger kids who come in for daycare.

 Community need: _____

What I can do to help fill this need: _____

_____

_____

 Community need: _____

What I can do to help fill this need: _____

_____

_____

 Community need: _____

What I can do to help fill this need: _____

_____

_____

In the middle of difficulty,
lies opportunity.

—ALBERT EINSTEIN

Taste-Berry Decisions:
Sharing Your Talents

The meaning of life is finding your gift;
the purpose of life is giving it away.
—JOY J. GOLLIVER

What does this quote mean to you?

_____

_____

_____

_____

Gifts and talents are meant to be shared. Do you play the piano, draw or paint? You can share these talents with seniors or children, or by volunteering to perform in fund-raisers. If art is your talent, your creativity can be used for community murals and posters and brochures for any number of community-service organizations. If you have a gift for reading, there are people who can't see well enough to read, such as those recovering from illness who would love for you to read to them. Even being able to walk can be your gift to give to someone in a wheelchair who could use your assistance.

List three gifts and talents you possess, and how you might be able to share them with others:

1 _____

_____

_____

2 _____

_____

_____

3 _____

_____

_____

The desire to uplift the spirit of others
is an indication of one's own
happy spirit.

—BETTIE B. YOUNGS

Taste-Berry Actions:
Sharing Your Talents

What other ways can you be of service? Use your Yellow Pages or go to the library to look up which organizations in your area do the kind of work you'd most like to volunteer to do.

List them below:

♡ _____

_____

♡ _____

_____

♡ _____

_____

♡ _____

_____

♡ _____

_____

♡ _____

_____

♡ _____

_____

Taste-Berry Decisions:
Making the World a Better Place

A reporter once asked Mother Teresa, one of the greatest "taste berries" of our times, what she considered to be the single most important thing we can do to make the world a better place. Her answer was simply, "Begin with one single act of kindness—in your family, in your community and everywhere you go. Just begin . . . one, one, one."

What do you think Mother Teresa meant when she said this?

_____

_____

_____

_____

_____

_____

_____

Maybe you can't make the lives of all the children without parents in your city better, but you can become a Big Brother or Big Sister to one boy or girl. Even if our actions affect only one person, that is enough to make a difference.

Begin by doing something nice in your own home—by being a better brother or sister, for example. When you see your younger brother or sister frustrated with his or her homework, offer to help.

Keep a shopping bag in your closet and when you outgrow an item or decide you'll never use it, put it in the bag. Once the bag is full, drop it off at a homeless shelter. And when you see someone down on his or her luck, share a kind word to build his or her self-worth. It makes a difference in the world, as society benefits from that person's increased self-esteem. Never forget that even the seemingly small things you do can make a difference to all our brothers and sisters the world over.

Use this space to brainstorm ways you can make a difference:

♡ _____

♡ _____

♡ _____

♡ _____

♡ _____

♡ _____

♡ _____

♡ _____

♡ _____

♡ _____

♡ _____

Taste-Berry Actions:
Making the World a Better Place

You must be the change you wish
to see in the world.

—GANDHI

What does this quote mean to you?

If changing the world begins with you, if you must "be the change you wish to see in the world," what would you change in yourself before you begin?

Taste-Berry Decisions: Encouraging Others

Citizen of the Year

My school held an annual end-of-the-year awards assembly to recognize those students who stood out because of their exceptional performance in sports, academics, extracurricular activities or who brought honor to the school in some way. As each award was handed out, the audience clapped, hooted, whistled and cheered wildly. Finally came the award for best citizenship, to be given to the person who had most contributed in a positive and significant way to our school.

The award went to Kevin Lloyd. He was not only on the football team, but was also student body vice president and president of Youth for a Better Tomorrow. Kevin leaped up on stage with his customary enthusiasm and charisma. "Thanks," he said in the midst of our applause. "This is an honor, thank you. I appreciate this honor, everyone—but," his voice rose to quiet the applause, "there's someone who deserves this more than I do."

The crowd grew silent at his unexpected words. "Someone who spends more hours at this school than any of us. Someone who gets here before we do, and he's here long after we're gone. Someone who has attended just about every special event, every game this school has held. You name it, he's there, cheering the team on. And he never lets that get in the way of offering a helping hand or giving a word of encouragement to any of us, either. I could go on and on, but I don't need to. I'm sure you all know who I'm talking about—Mr. Paul—and I'd like to give this award to him."

Rising to their feet, the audience went wild, chanting, "Mr. Paul! Mr. Paul! Mr. Paul!"

That day, Mr. Paul, our school's tireless and dedicated custodian, was named our Citizen of the Year to enthusiastic whoops of applause and approval. Mr. Paul, with tears in his eyes, walked up and accepted the award, his words simple. "Thank you so much. I've only done two important things in my whole entire life. The first was serving this fine school in a job I've loved. And the second was having you share this award with me, because it makes me realize that you know I love you all as much as I do." With that, Mr. Paul, who in just three months would retire from the school district, stepped down. With his eyes still teary— and a smile that stretched from ear to ear—he held the plastic award as though it were a precious crystal. It was the only time he'd ever been publicly recognized for his dedication, his consistently thorough work, his endless acts of giving, and for a lifetime of service to others.

Remember, though, it took someone thoughtful and kind and secure in himself, like Kevin Lloyd, to make it happen.

—Jennifer Leigh Youngs, *Taste Berries for Teens*

Would you have done what Kevin Lloyd did? Why?

?
_____

_____

_____

_____

_____

_____

_____

How did Kevin Lloyd's giving his award to Mr. Paul make a "difference"? To whom besides Mr. Paul did it make a difference?

➤
_____

_____

_____

_____

_____

_____

_____

_____

_____

_____

_____

Taste-Berry Actions:
Encouraging Others

Letting someone know how much you appreciate his or her service to others is not only thoughtful, but it also encourages that person to continue to do those kind things. Collectively, all these kind and thoughtful actions make the world a more loving place in which to live. It's like a chain reaction—one candle of good being used to light the next candle of good, and then the next, and the next, and so on, until a great glow of light has been created from the flame of just one little candle.

List three people who have been extraordinarily thoughtful to you, and how they've shown it. Then, decide what is the best way you can thank each of these people for their kindness.

EXAMPLE:

Who: My friend Tara.

How: She gives me a ride to school each morning.

How I show appreciation: I make sure I'm on time so I don't make her late for school and thank her every day for giving me a ride.

♥ Who: _____

How he/she shows thoughtfulness: _____

_____

How I show appreciation: _____

_____

_____

_____

_____

♥ Who: _____

How he/she shows thoughtfulness: _____

_____

How I show appreciation: _____

_____

_____

_____

_____

♥ Who: _____

How he/she shows thoughtfulness: _____

_____

How I show appreciation: _____

_____

_____

_____

_____

Taste-Berry Decisions: Gratitude

I live in a nice house and have so many comforts. Still, I'm always saying I don't have anything to wear, or that I need this, or can't live without that. Then I volunteered to help out on a soup line, and I saw that so many people were without even the basics. The experience showed me that I shouldn't take things for granted.

—Erin Bishop, 16, *Taste Berries for Teens*

Gratitude becomes a circle of love. When we help others, we become more grateful for the good we have in our lives. And when we feel grateful, we're looking at all the good in our lives and feeling as if we have plenty. We want to give to others.

What are all the things you are grateful for?

EXAMPLE:

♡ My parents love me.

♡ I live in a safe neighborhood.

♡ I have my own room.

♡ I have friends.

♡ I get to go to school.

My Gratitude List . . .

✔ _____
✔ _____
✔ _____
✔ _____
✔ _____
✔ _____
✔ _____
✔ _____
✔ _____
✔ _____
✔ _____
✔ _____
✔ _____
✔ _____
✔ _____
✔ _____
✔ _____
✔ _____

If you realize that you have enough,
you are truly rich.

—TAO TE CHING

Taste-Berry Decisions:
Act Locally, Think Globally

The Shirt Off His Back

Feeling a tap on his shoulder while in the middle of distributing food and supplies to people with a group of other workers, eighteen-year-old Toby Long turned around to find an Ethiopian boy standing behind him. Gaunt and looking very tired, the young boy looked first at his own tattered shirt then at Toby's clothes. Next, he asked if he could have Toby's shirt. Toby had traveled to Africa to work for two-and-a-half weeks with World Vision, an organization dedicated to alleviating hunger and suffering around the world. He had a long day of work in the hot sun before him, and wouldn't get back to his camp until night. Toby didn't know what to say to the little boy other than, "I need it, too."

When Toby returned to camp that evening he couldn't stop thinking about the little boy with the big sad eyes, a small child who also spent his days in the scorching hot sun. A boy so desperately in need of a shirt—Toby's shirt. Hunger wasn't the only problem in this area where poverty loomed everywhere. Most people had only one or two ragged pieces of clothing to their name. Haunted by the memory of the boy—and his own refusal to give him his shirt—Toby cried about the decision he'd made. But not for long. Toby vowed not to forget the boy he had denied his shirt.

With the memory of the boy burning in his heart, when Toby returned home to Michigan, he made good on his promise to make a difference in the lives of the people he had seen: He organized a T-shirt drive in his community! Called "Give the Shirt Off Your Back," Toby's campaign soon collected over ten thousand T-shirts.

"I think we can all make a difference," said Toby. "One of the things that I've struggled with is wondering if that little boy I met will get one of the ten thousand shirts, and I don't know the answer. But I can pray that he does—or that someone who receives one will give it to him should he ask."

Toby's giving isn't just limited to those he directly helps; his example of how one teen with a sincere desire and determination can make a difference in the world serves as a gift of inspiration to many others.

—Jennifer Leigh Youngs, *Taste Berries for Teens*

What do you think about Toby? Why would he be a great guy to have as your friend?

_____

_____

_____

_____

_____

_____

Taste-Berry Actions:
Think Globally, Act Locally

What do you think that it means to "think globally, but act locally"?

_____

_____

_____

_____

To "act locally" can mean helping out in your family, within your circle of friends, or in your school or neighborhood. List three ways you act locally, and how it makes a difference in the world.

1 _____

_____

2 _____

_____

3 _____

_____

Your Greatest Contribution to the World

What do you think your greatest contribution in life will be—the one that will make the biggest difference in the world and change it in the biggest way?

_____
_____
_____

How will you be remembered for this contribution?

_____
_____
_____

Is it important to you that others recognize what you do to make a difference? Why?

_____
_____
_____

As a woman, my country is the whole world.

—VIRGINIA WOOLF

Coping with Embarrassing Moments, Hurt Feelings, Moods, Stress and Other Tough Stuff

Trying times can teach us to be compassionate to those we meet throughout our lives—and that's what being a "taste berry" is all about.

—*Taste Berries for Teens*

Embarrassing Moments

Just Three Leaves!

I wanted everything to be perfect for my prom.

At our school, everyone makes a big deal about having a beautiful corsage, so I wanted mine to be really really special. I wanted a Casablanca Easter Lily, a large, white, very beautiful flower, as my corsage. I told my boyfriend what I wanted and, sure enough, it's what he got me. I was positively thrilled! I just knew everyone at the prom would be talking about my corsage!

When my boyfriend arrived with the corsage, my parents and little sister ooohed and ahhhed and then began taking pictures. First, they took pictures of "the" flower still encased in its plastic container, then of my boyfriend as he was taking the flower out of its plastic shrine, then of me holding the flower. There were pictures of the flower being pinned on my dress and yet another of me, my boyfriend and the flower. "Stand closer to 'the flower,'" my mother said to him.

When we left for the prom, I was as proud as I could be! My boyfriend, "the flower" and I were about to begin a wonderful and memorable evening. Everyone looked at each other's flower corsages. I was certain mine was the most beautiful. Even so, I tried to be very modest. I was careful to stand up straight, and tried not to look in the direction of the lily; after all, it spoke for itself. When I did occasionally peek nonchalantly down at my corsage, I saw the beautiful ferns, ribbons and greenery all spraying grandly forth and rested assured my gorgeous Casablanca Easter Lily, though obstructed from my own view, was fittingly framed in its splendor for all other eyes to see.

I was certain that my corsage caught the attention of just about everyone, because nearly all of them said something. "Very interesting!" MaryJane Harriman said, jealous I'm sure. "Hey, great corsage!" Sheila Henry said. "Impressive," Janet Stephenson said. "Everyone says I've got to get a closer look at your flower," Cathy Jones announced. Many of the girls just looked and smiled, not knowing what to say. It was a memorable evening, made sweeter by the fact that I had been the center of attention!

Finally, when the band was preparing to play their last song, Mr. Thomas, the principal, got up on the stage and announced, "We are so happy this year's event has been a success. Just one short announcement. Will whoever dropped her corsage take it with you as you leave; we've been holding it since before the band played their first set, thinking someone would claim it." Frowning down at the bloom in his hand, he held up a bedraggled flower—my Casablanca Easter Lily.

I was mortified! To my horror, my wish for everyone talking about my corsage had come true! All evening I had been wearing a corsage consisting only of ribbons, a spray of ferns and three green leaves, and all the while I'd been calling attention to it!

—Tamara Wilson, 18, *Taste Berries for Teens*

What should Tamara say to those who tease her about her "great corsage" when she sees them at school?

_____

_____

_____

_____

_____

_____

_____

_____

_____

_____

_____

_____

*You will do foolish things, but
do them with enthusiasm.*

—COLETTE

What's the Most Embarrassing Thing That's Ever Happened to You?

What is the most embarrassing thing that's ever happened to you? How old were you when it happened? Who was involved? What were the circumstances?

_____

_____

_____

_____

_____

_____

Why was this incident so embarrassing? How did you feel about what happened—were you humiliated at the time or were you able to laugh about it?

_____

_____

_____

_____

_____

_____

How did it turn out in the end? What did you do? How did you get through it? How did you "survive"?

_____

_____

_____

_____

_____

Did you get over your embarrassment quickly or is it still with you now? Looking back, how do you feel about it?

_____

_____

_____

_____

_____

How did your friends feel about it? Did your friends know about it? Did you and your friends discuss it? Do they ever bring it up?

_____

_____

_____

_____

_____

Taste-Berry Actions:
Surviving Embarrassing Moments

Even though you may not think so at the time, an embarrassing moment can be a good teacher. For example, it can teach you to have empathy for others when they're caught in an embarrassing predicament. What was the biggest lesson your most embarrassing moment taught you?

_____

_____

_____

_____

_____

What was the most important thing it taught you about yourself?

_____

_____

_____

_____

Give up to grace. The ocean takes care
of each wave till it gets to shore.

—RUMI

My Crush on Damon Brunner

I had a huge crush on Damon Brunner. When he asked me out, I was very excited and wanted to look really great. I decided my best friend's flowered skirt was the perfect thing to wear—even though my friend was a size smaller than I was.

We went to see a movie. All was going well until I took my seat in the theater, and that's when disaster struck: The zipper on the beautiful little skirt gave way. I was upset, first because this was my friend's skirt, but worse, I had no idea how I was going to get from the theater to the car without my skirt falling to the ground. My worries didn't end there. The movie over, my elbows glued to my side as we walked to the parking lot, Damon and I ran into some of our friends from school. They were all going out for a pizza and asked us to join them. Of course I said no, and told them I had a huge test tomorrow and needed to study which didn't make sense since some of them, including Damon, were in the same classes at school as I was."Well, okay, see you tomorrow," they said, and even Damon didn't seem to mind that we weren't going with them, so I just knew that everyone could see my problem, and though being nice now, they'd tease me about it the next day at school. And, I was quite sure that this whole zipper thing would be the end of my chances with Damon Brunner.

I hardly slept at all that night. And knowing that there was no way to avoid running into my friends at school didn't make me exactly anxious to get to school the next

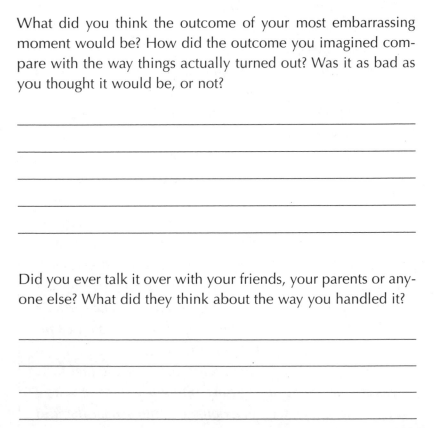

day. Well, the morning arrived and I did go to school. But you know what? Damon said he'd had a nice time, and asked me out for the following weekend! And no one at school ever mentioned the broken zipper. Maybe they hadn't even noticed—or if they did, they didn't make as big a deal out of it as I did. As I discovered, things aren't always as bad as they seem.

—Lea Rosen, 17, *Taste Berries for Teens*

What did you think the outcome of your most embarrassing moment would be? How did the outcome you imagined compare with the way things actually turned out? Was it as bad as you thought it would be, or not?

_____

_____

_____

_____

_____

Did you ever talk it over with your friends, your parents or anyone else? What did they think about the way you handled it?

_____

_____

_____

_____

Embarrassing Moments . . . and
Empathy for Others

Write about a time you saw a really good friend going through an embarrassing moment. What happened? What did you do? Did you try to help her or him? Did you feel for her? How did things turn out? Were the two of you able to talk about it later, maybe even laugh about it? Or, did the incident remain "off limits" to talk about or bring up?

_____

_____

_____

_____

_____

_____

_____

_____

_____

*Every forest branch moves
differently in the breeze, but as they
sway they connect at the roots.*

—RUMI

Hurt Feelings

More Perfect than Others

At Jefferson High School the junior class spon-sors the annual Junior-Senior Spring Prom. On the first school day in October, the new class of eleventh-grade students holds a fund-raiser to earn the money necessary to put on the event. The fund-raiser is known as "Gofer Day," where the juniors are auctioned off: They "sell" themselves to members of the senior class for the day. A "gofer" can be purchased for the purpose of doing any task deemed reasonable—such as cleaning out a locker. The auction is held in the school's large auditorium, with the entire school present. Each individual student is auctioned off, one by one, to the "highest bidder."

No one bid on Angeline. "It made me feel that no one liked me," she said, her feelings hurt. "I cried about it because it showed me I'm not very popular. I know it's because of my weight. I'm smart and a really good singer, but my talent and good grades aren't enough to make me popular. But what really upsets me is that some of the kids will make snide remarks about my weight to my face, like calling me 'chubs' and stuff. Even when it's coming from friends who are just saying it in fun, it still hurts, even if they smile or laugh when they say it. On days when I'm feeling good, I can take it. But on days when I'm not feel-ing so great, it makes me sad enough to cry.

"I don't want to go around being upset at everyone for not bidding on me, but I still needed an apology—if only make believe. So to soothe my heart, I had them write me a letter of apology. Well actually, I did it for them! Here's what it said:"

Dear Angeline,

Isn't it nice to know that there are people who admire you not only for the way you are but for who you are becoming? We think you are a great talent and a good friend. And remember, a bid doesn't reflect your worth. We think you are priceless and we are embarrassed to admit that no one that day could afford you!

Love,

Everyone at Jefferson High!

—Taste Berries for Teens

It's such a secret place, the land of tears.

—ANTOINE DE SAINT-EXUPÉRY

Why do you think we shed tears when we are sad?

_____

_____

_____

Have You Ever Had Your Feelings Hurt?

Have you ever had your feelings hurt? Write about an incident where you had your feelings hurt. What happened? Who hurt your feelings? Did that person know it? How do you know? What did the person do to hurt your feelings?

_____

_____

_____

_____

How did you feel about what happened? How did you work it out and get through the hurt? Does it still hurt today? Why?

_____

_____

_____

_____

Did you have any part in getting your feelings hurt? What could you have done differently to avoid getting hurt?

_____

_____

_____

_____

Does Someone Owe You an Apology?

If you could have the person who hurt your feelings write an apology letter to you, what would it say? Write the perfect letter of apology from that person to you—one that would make all the hurt go away.

Dear _____ ,

I'd like to tell you how sorry I am for . . .

⬛ _____

_____

_____

_____

_____

_____

_____

_____

_____

_____

_____

_____

_____

_____

_____

Comforting Yourself When Your Feelings Are Hurt

Sometimes others do things and say things to us that we don't deserve. When that happens, we can let them know that they have hurt our feelings. Sometimes they'll apologize; other times, they won't. But even if they don't, we can't forget to treat ourselves with respect and kindness, to be *our own* best friend.

Remember to root for yourself—especially during those times when you're struggling with hurt feelings. For example, if someone says you shouldn't even bother trying out for cheerleading, the football team or a role in the school play, you can say you're going to give it a try and hope for the best! Or, if someone makes fun of your less-than-perfect grade on a test, you can say you're studying more now and you know you'll do better next time.

List three ways you can comfort and encourage yourself when others have been less than thoughtful, when the chips are down, or when hope seems lost:

1 _____

_____

2 _____

_____

3 _____

_____

Getting Comfort When Your Feelings Are Hurt

Happiness does not depend on outward things,
but on the way we see them.

—LEO TOLSTOY

What does this quote mean to you?

_____

_____

_____

_____

Sometimes when our feelings are hurt, we can go inside to that little place where we comfort ourselves. Sometimes this is good, but it's also important to turn to people we trust to help us sort things out, and to offer encouragement and advice.

When your feelings are hurt, who can you turn to for help with sorting it out? List five people who support you, what they do that is so helpful and how their support helps you work through hurt feelings.

EXAMPLE:

<u>Who:</u> My father.

<u>What my father does that is so helpful:</u> He treats me extra kindly, talking to me in a soft tone of voice and allowing me some extra time on the phone to talk to my friends.

<u>How this helps:</u> My dad's giving me extra time on the phone helps me work things out by talking them over with my friends. My dad's being sensitive to what I'm going through makes me feel like my dad really understands me and loves me—so I feel better.

♥ Who: _____

What the person does that is so helpful: _____

_____

_____

How this helps: _____

_____

_____

♥ Who: _____

What the person does that is so helpful: _____

_____

_____

How this helps: _____

_____

_____

♥ Who: _____

What the person does that is so helpful: _____

_____

_____

How this helps: _____

_____

_____

♥ Who: _____

What the person does that is so helpful: _____

_____

_____

How this helps: _____

_____

_____

♥ Who: _____

What the person does that is so helpful: _____

_____

_____

How this helps: _____

_____

_____

If you have a pet, does it recognize when your feelings are hurt? How is your pet sensitive to you at these times?

EXAMPLE:

<u>Who:</u> My dog.

<u>What my pet does that is so helpful:</u> He notices the change in my mood, and looks at me with his head tilted as though he understands. As soon as he sees that I get this, he runs over to be petted and this makes me feel better.

<u>How this helps:</u> I stop thinking about my hurt for a moment and instead, feel my love for my dog. His affection and playfulness are welcome relief from my hurt feelings. At those times, I love my doggie even more, and at the same time, I love me a little more. This makes me feel more hopeful—like I'm lovable—and so I stop being so hard on myself and lighten up a little.

Who: _____

What my pet does that is so helpful: _____

_____

_____

How this helps: _____

_____

_____

Nobody sees a flower, really—
it is so small. We haven't time, and to
see takes time, like to have a
friend takes time.

—GEORGIA O'KEEFFE

What does this quote mean to you?

_____

_____

_____

_____

_____

_____

_____

_____

_____

_____

_____

_____

_____

Feeling Moody

Mostly

A father and his two kids noticed the cat (who lay asleep) in the pet supply store and hurried over to stroke him. Startled, the surprised cat hissed defensively at them. The beautiful kitty then shuffled around in the little nest atop the little perch, turning his body from the comfortable position he was in to one in which he could keep an eye on passersby. Now that he was alert and attentive to all going on around him—and looking uneasy—it was easy to see that he'd like these interlopers to leave him alone.

It worked. The father, making remarks about the "unfriendly" cat, led his two sons away.

You see, the proud plump cat was born with only three legs. The nerve endings of the missing leg are so close to the surface, it pains him, and so he protects it. He's not an unsociable or unfriendly kitty. In fact, he's mostly a very social and very friendly cat. It's one of the many reasons the store owner named him Mostly. "He's a kitty that didn't come with all his parts, but mostly he did!" the store owner says. "Sometimes my kitty doesn't like to be touched, but mostly he does. Some people—mostly those who are insensitive to the needs, moods and whims of others—think he's just a cantankerous kitty. But in fact, Mostly is a very lovable and adorable cat. So, we call him Mostly!"

—*Taste Berries for Teens*

Mostly wants to be petted on his own terms—when his painful side is tucked safely beneath him. Of course, it was impossible for strangers to know this. Moods are like that; it's mostly impossible to read someone else's mind.

Have you ever had someone think you were upset, when you really weren't?

❑ Yes ❑ No

Maybe you were feeling moody, even though you didn't know why you were feeling this way. You just knew you needed a little "space" to let it pass. Does that ever happen to you? If you had to give these moments a name, what would it be? "Off"? "Grumpy"? "Touchy"? "Irritable"? "Reflective"? What?

✔ _____

✔ _____

✔ _____

✔ _____

✔ _____

✔ _____

We grow in time to trust the
future for our answers.

—RUTH BENEDICT

Do You Have Days When You Just "Need a Break"?

Moods are mostly about "on our terms." Whether or not we know the reason behind them, we appreciate it when others are sensitive to us. Sometimes we just need others to respect the time we need to work through them and, in the meantime, be sensitive and understanding—even gentle with us. Like when you're having one of those days when everything just seems to go wrong and a friend or your mom or dad notices and allows you your mood—without demanding a change in attitude. That can be a loving gift.

Write about a time when you were really moody and someone "gave you a break" by giving you the space to work it out for yourself. What was going on that contributed to your being moody? Did you know the reason for your mood? What caused it? How were you feeling at the time?

_____

_____

_____

_____

_____

_____

_____

_____

Who was it who gave you the space you needed? Did it change the way you felt about the person, or did you already trust this person would respect your moods? What were your "new" feelings for the person?

♥ _____

_____

_____

_____

What did you learn about yourself from the incident? What did you learn about the other person? What did you learn about your moods or about moods in general?

♥ _____

_____

_____

_____

How do you react when one of your parents or friends seems a little "moody"? Are you willing to be sensitive to their needs and be patient until they are able to work themselves back into a better mood?

♥ _____

_____

_____

_____

When You're Feeling Moody, How Do You Wish to Be Treated?

You want others to be sensitive to your moods, but being sensitive can mean different things to different people. How do *you* like others to deal with you when you're feeling "out of sorts"? Do you prefer they leave you alone, cheer you up, comfort you, ignore the mood without ignoring you, humor you? Write what you prefer and why you prefer it.

_____

_____

_____

_____

_____

_____

_____

Who would you most like to have take to heart what you've written? Do you think you will share your feelings with this person? Why?

_____

_____

_____

How does being dealt with this way work for you? Is it effective? For example, if you prefer to go in your room and sort out your feelings alone, does that work, or do you really need to talk with someone to work things through?

_____

_____

_____

_____

When you're in a "bad mood" do you say one thing, but mean another? For example, if you tell your friends at school to leave you alone for awhile, explaining you don't want to talk about whatever it is you are upset about at this time—that you need a little "space"—is that what you really want? Or does being left alone only make you feel really alone, deserted and lonely, and you really would like your friends to not leave you alone, but rather, come to your "rescue," to help you through your situation? Do you ask for what you need, or hope others will read your mind and know exactly what you want? How can you communicate your needs to others effectively?

_____

_____

_____

_____

_____

_____

_____

> *Being a teenager can be a confusing time. One minute you're feeling up. The next you're feeling down. Things are terrific one day and in the pits the next. And, you really don't understand why.*
>
> —Taste Berries for Teens

How do you relate to this quote?

_____

_____

_____

_____

_____

_____

_____

*The trouble with life isn't
that there is no answer. It's that there
are so many answers.*

—ANAÏS NIN

Getting Comfort When You're Feeling Moody

List three people who are sensitive to your moods and can help you work through them. What do they say and do that helps you work through your moods?

EXAMPLE:

<u>Who:</u> My mother.

<u>Helpful approach:</u> She gives me space but tells me, "Let me know when you want to talk about it."

♥ Who: _____

Helpful approach: _____

_____

_____

♥ Who: _____

Helpful approach: _____

_____

_____

♥ Who: _____

Helpful approach: _____

_____

_____

Stressing Out

You Snooze, You Lose!

I set my alarm for seven o'clock in the morning, but when it went off, I hit the snooze button, thinking I'd catch five more minutes of sleep. The snooze alarm didn't go off!

When I looked over and saw that it was 7:45, I couldn't believe it! I skipped breakfast so I could run to catch the bus, but I missed it anyway. Luckily, my father hadn't left for work yet, so I asked him for a ride to school. He wasn't too happy about it because it meant he would be late for an appointment he had set up. We rode to school in dead silence.

By the time I got to school, the five-minute bell had already rung, so I had to go to the office to get a late pass. I hadn't asked my father to write a note for my being late, so I sat out first hour in the principal's office. By now, things were really starting to snowball. Since I was absent from my first-hour class, I missed my science test. My teacher said I couldn't make up the test since I had an unexcused absence. When I went to my locker to get my books for my second-hour class, my math book was missing. My locker-mate, Barney Johnson, had picked up my book instead of his own. I was frantic. I hadn't turned in my math assignment the day before, and Mr. Cohen warned me not to let it happen again. My overdue math paper was in the book Barney had, and I had no idea where he could be, so, rather than face the teacher, I decided to skip math class! The math teacher took attendance, and because I wasn't reported on the absence list the vice principal called my mother at work to tell her that I wasn't in school. When I got to third-hour class, my friends teased me about my whereabouts during second hour. I was in no mood for their humor. "Why don't you just worry about yourself," I snapped. "Who do you think you are, a truant officer?" Being upset with my friends always makes me feel bad.

Standing in the lunch line, I noticed Barney Johnson. "Hey, Johnson! You took my math book, you idiot!" I called out. Barney yelled back, "Get off my back, you jerk!" At the end of my rope, I shoved Barney against the wall, my fist raised ready to hit him—when who should appear but the vice principal! Surprised to see me, he ordered me to get away from Barney, informed me about the call he made earlier to my mother and took me to the office. Knowing my mother had been told that I wasn't in school made me feel even more stressed out. I knew she was going to call my father and tell him, too. Since I wasn't allowed to leave the office because I was in trouble for fighting, I wasn't able to make a call from the hall pay phone, either.

Finally, the school day was over. What a nightmare. And I still had to face my parents! Deciding to just be honest, I told them the whole story.

"Let's talk about what you might've done to make it less difficult," my mom suggested. "Sounds like your day was tough, all right," my dad said. "I guess I don't have to remind you anymore that when you snooze, you lose."

— Rob Lawson, 15, *Taste Berries for Teens*

How Do You Handle the Stress?

Write about a time when you were really worried about a problem or situation you were going through. What were you worried about? What was the problem or situation? Why were you so worried?

_____

_____

_____

_____

_____

Do you ever create your own stress?

❑ Yes ❑ No

If you do, how? What do you do that adds to the stress you already feel?

_____

_____

_____

_____

_____

In the previous situation, what happened? How did you cope with things? What might've been an even better way to deal with it?

_____

_____

_____

_____

_____

_____

_____

_____

_____

How did you identify your worry as stress? How did you know it was "stress" you were feeling?

_____

_____

_____

_____

_____

_____

_____

How did things turn out in the end? What actually happened, what came true? What are your feelings about it now? For example, do you think back and say, "It sure *seemed* worse at the time than it does now"?

_____

_____

_____

_____

Sometimes we think things are more of a disaster than they really are—and many times the solution is easier than we might think. Was that true in this incident? Explain.

_____

_____

_____

_____

Don't sweat the small stuff.

—Richard Carlson

What does this quote mean to you?

_____

_____

_____

The expression, "Don't make a mountain out of a molehill" means to not blow things out of proportion, not to think things are worse than they really are. But consider for a moment that the worst did happen, the molehill you were worrying over really did turn into a mountain. Did you survive it? For example, if you had hoped that your not studying for a certain test wouldn't mean you would fail it—but you did—did the world go on anyway? Explain.

?
_____

_____

_____

_____

_____

_____

Deciding that the world won't end is a real breakthrough. Even so, sometimes you can't make it to the other side of stress alone, and you need help and support for what you are going through. List five people you can turn to for help during those stressful times, especially when the molehill really is a mountain.

♡ _____

♡ _____

♡ _____

♡ _____

♡ _____

From Cool to Ghoul:
Do You Ever Lose Your Cool?

When you're stressed out, do you look as though any moment there could be steam coming from your ears? Are the words "Stressed Out!" stamped on your forehead? How do you act? For example, our friend Tawny is a very reserved and quiet person. When she is "stressed to the max" she becomes even more quiet and reserved. When our friend Jessica, who is also a very shy and quiet person, is stressed out, she lets you know about it—often getting frantic. How do you act? What do you do? Describe what you look like under stress.

?
_____

_____

_____

_____

_____

_____

_____

_____

Simplicity, patience, compassion.
These are the greatest
treasures.

—*Tao Te Ching*

How Much Do You Pay for Stress?

What "price do you pay" for being under stress? For example, do you find it difficult to concentrate? Does thinking about your problem keep you from paying close attention to all the things you were supposed to be doing—like staying on top of your schoolwork and keeping promises and commitments?

Stress affects us physically, emotionally and behaviorally. Put a check mark beside those "side effects" that apply to you. Then list other ways you respond when you're under stress.

How stress affects me *physically:*

♡ My muscles get tense.

♡ My hands get cold or sweaty.

♡ My stomach feels as if it is churning.

♡ I have difficulty sleeping.

♡ My heart beats rapidly.

♡ I have sudden bursts of energy.

♡ I am extremely tired.

♡ I lose my appetite, or eat too much.

♡ _____

♡ _____

♡ _____

♡ _____

How stress affects me *emotionally:*

♡ I get nervous.

♡ I cry.

♡ I want to strike out or hit something.

♡ I feel sad.

♡ I giggle a lot.

♡ I worry excessively and can't stop thinking, "what if."

♡ I am irritable or feel depressed.

♡ I feel bad about myself.

♡ I daydream a lot at school (or have bad dreams at night).

♡ I get angry easily, sometimes even to the point of being explosive.

♡ I lose interest in my appearance.

♡ _____

♡ _____

♡ _____

♡ _____

How stress affects my *behavior:*

♡ I have difficulty concentrating.

♡ I substitute food, drugs or alcohol for coping.

♡ I become grouchy, irritable, even mean.

♡ I cover up by not being honest about something.

♡ I get into arguments or fights with others.

♡ I deliberately do sloppy work (not caring about how it is done).

♡ I procrastinate.

♡ I smile a lot to cover up my feelings.

♡ I ignore my feelings, hoping they will go away.

♡ _____

♡ _____

♡ _____

♡ _____

*The most difficult years in life
are those between ten
and seventy.*

—HELEN HAYES

From Ghoul to Cool:
Getting Back in Control

How you respond to a situation—rather than the situation itself—is really the deciding factor in how much stress you experience. In short, *you* get to determine how stressed-out you become.

Don't let your stress change you from cool to ghoul. Think positive thoughts—and not negative thoughts!

One simple way to do this is called *thought stopping*. What this means is you visualize a stop sign whenever you start to get negative. This stop sign acts as a signal for you to stop thinking a negative thought and to replace it with a positive one, one that points you in a positive direction.

EXAMPLE:

Negative Message: "My hair is so boring!" you say, noticing a friend's new hairstyle.

The moment you say this, immediately say, "Stop!" Then correct yourself by changing the negative to a positive.

Positive Message: "I've been wearing my hair like this for a long time and I'm really ready for a change."

Changing or "rewriting" the way you think about something is a good way to stop focusing on the negatives and the "what if's." Instead, focus on what you can do to change the situation in a positive way.

How? Replace the negative thinking with a positive and constructive thought, one that points you in a better direction.

EXAMPLE:

Positive Message: "I've been wearing my hair like this for a long time and I'm really ready for a change."

Positive Action: "I'm going to start saving up my money so that by the end of this month I will have a new, more trendy style."

EXAMPLE:

Negative Message: "I don't have any friends."

Rewrite-Positive Message: "I'd like to be friends with Amber, but she doesn't seem to want me as a friend. Still, Jenaye is a very good friend to me, and I have a lot of other friends, as well."

Positive Action: "I'm just going to focus on being a good friend to the people who are my friends."

Now you try it. Write down three negative messages you tell yourself, and then rewrite them to reflect a positive direction:

STOP Negative Message: _____

Rewrite-Positive Message: _____

_____

_____

♡ Positive Action: _____

_____

_____

STOP Negative Message: _____

Rewrite-Positive Message: _____

_____

_____

♡ Positive Action: _____

_____

_____

STOP Negative Message: _____

Rewrite-Positive Message: _____

_____

_____

♡ Positive Action: _____

_____

_____

Taste-Berry Actions:
Being Good to Yourself

When things seem really stressful, it's time to be extra good to yourself—get adequate rest, eat properly and get the exercise your body needs to burn off tension. Write down ten practical ways for you to deal with stressful times.

EXAMPLE:

♡ I'll exercise to burn off tension.

♡ I'll make sure I eat good foods.

♡ I'll make sure I spend time with my friends.

1 _____

2 _____

3 _____

4 _____

5 _____

6 _____

7 _____

8 _____

9 _____

10 _____

*The big question is whether
you're going to give a big hearty
yes to your adventure.*

—JOSEPH CAMPBELL

Painful Times

Tell Me "Why?"

Please God, tell me why
Friends have to die.
It's not fair and it's not right.
Oh God, why that night?

I didn't think life could end so fast.
She was so young but her years didn't last.
Now it's too late to say good-bye.
Please God, tell me, "Why?"

Even if her soul is flying free,
Now her dreams can never be.
Teens aren't supposed to die.
I need an answer, God. Please, tell me, "Why?"

Maybe life isn't what it seems,
And not all teens get their dreams.
I know we're all meant to someday die,
Still God, I have to ask you, "Why?"

—Peggy Nunziata, 16, *Taste Berries for Teens*

Do you ever wonder "why" we feel pain? Why do you suppose we do? What purpose do you suppose it serves?

_____

_____

_____

_____

_____

_____

_____

_____

_____

_____

_____

_____

_____

_____

There are years that ask questions,
and years that answer.

—ZORA NEALE HURSTON

Have You Ever Faced a Really Painful Time?

What is the most painful experience you've ever faced? How did you get through it? What did you do? Who did you turn to for comfort and help in sorting it out, or did you go through it alone?

?
_____

_____

_____

_____

_____

_____

How would you have handled going through the same experience today? Would you do anything differently? Would you turn to the *same* person or people for help? Why?

_____

_____

_____

_____

_____

_____

Have you ever lost someone close to you to death? Were you sad, angry, scared, all of these and more? What were your feelings at the time?

_____

_____

_____

_____

_____

_____

How did you express your feelings? Did you keep them inside? Did you let others know what you were feeling?

_____

_____

_____

_____

_____

_____

Where there is sorrow, there
is holy ground.

—OSCAR WILDE

Saying Good-Bye

How did you say good-bye? Use this space to write a letter of good-bye to the person you lost:

Dear _____,

_____

_____

_____

_____

_____

_____

_____

_____

_____

_____

_____

I know how much you miss me,
I see the pain within your heart;
But I'm really not so far away,
We really aren't apart.

—ARLENE BURRES

Taste-Berry Actions:
Taking Care of Yourself

*Pain may hurt, but it can also be a teacher. Pain
is a signal to take better care of yourself.*

—TASTE BERRIES FOR TEENS

What does this quote mean to you?

_____

_____

_____

_____

Sometimes we have days when everything about life seems
bleak. These are the times we need to be extra good to ourselves and reach out to the people we know will offer support
and understanding. Then we can use the difficult experience to
help us become more compassionate, loving and wise.

Write about a time when your pain led you to take better care
of yourself. How did you take better care of yourself? In what
ways were you stronger or wiser?

_____

_____

_____

_____

_____

_____

_____

_____

_____

_____

_____

_____

How has the experience helped you deal with tough issues today?

_____

_____

_____

_____

_____

_____

_____

_____

_____

Taste-Berry Actions:
Coping with Tough Times

When in the midst of heartache, we can often lose sight of the fact that those feelings of pain will pass. When trying to get away from feeling our pain, we want to be careful to choose healthy solutions and avoid making any unhealthy decisions.

Make a list of five healthy solutions that will help you get through the pain until the tough times pass:

1 ───────────────────────────

─────────────────────────────────

─────────────────────────────────

2 ───────────────────────────

─────────────────────────────────

─────────────────────────────────

3 ───────────────────────────

─────────────────────────────────

─────────────────────────────────

4 ───────────────────────────

─────────────────────────────────

─────────────────────────────────

5 ───────────────────────────

─────────────────────────────────

The cure for anything is salt water—
sweat, tears or the sea.

—ISAK DINESEN

When we are in the middle of our problems, it can be easy to forget all the many good things going on in our lives. But it's important to recall what's good in our lives. Not only does this help us through the hard times, but it can help us accept that there are going to be times of trial and tribulation—and that these, too, are a part of life. If you were to make a list of all the positive things in your life, as well as a list of all the negative, and then compare the two side by side, you might be surprised how the good outweighs the bad. For example, you might list homework on the negative side, but it could be canceled out by "getting an education" on the positive side. You might list that you have overly protective (strict) parents, but on the other side, list that you have parents who love you enough to care about your safety and well-being. You might list you've just broken off a friendship with someone special, but on the other side have any number of really good friends to list.

In painful times it's easy enough to list the negatives, but it's *a lot* more helpful to dwell on the positives. Make a list of all the *good* things about your life. When life seems to rain lemons, come back and visit this list and take note what a positive affect it will have on how you feel.

Positives in my life:

♡ _____

♡ _____

♡ _____

♡ _____

♡ _____

♡ _____

♡ _____

♡ _____

♡ _____

♡ _____

♡ _____

♡ _____

♡ _____

♡ _____

♡ _____

♡ _____

♡ _____

♡ _____

♡ _____

♡ _____

♡ _____

♡ _____

Picking Up the Pieces

When I was in ninth grade, a boy I was sure I was in love with started dating my best friend. One day he was walking me to my locker; and the next day, he was walking my very best friend to hers. "We're not going together any more!" he announced. "I'm going with Tammy now."

I didn't know what to think or how to feel. Should I be mad at him, or angry with my best friend? I was clear about one thing: I hurt all over. No one, not even my friends or parents really knew how deeply I was hurting. I didn't want to go to school. I didn't want to go to soccer practice. I didn't want to do anything. I just wanted to be alone. I didn't want to talk with anyone about it—certainly not my parents. Not that it stopped them from asking.

They asked anyway. "Would you like to talk about what's bothering you?" Mom asked. "No!" I cried.

"Talking can make it better," Mom reminded me. "It's just about my stupid best friend. I'll be okay," I said, hoping I didn't have to explain any more.

Mom didn't ask again, no doubt assuming that I'd tell her about it when I was ready. In the meantime, my parents were extra kind and tried to give me the space I needed; like a couple of times they allowed me to eat dinner in my room rather than coming to the dinner table. After about a week or so of my still being tearful, my mother stepped up her inspection of the issue. "I can see you are suffering over this," she said. "I think we should talk about it."

"Oh, Mom," I cried. "It hurts too much to talk about it!"
"Yes, honey," she soothed. "I can see that you are hurting."
"Why does it hurt so much?" I asked.
"Pain is God's way of saying your heart is broken."
"I don't need God to tell me my heart is broken," I cried.
"I just need him to fix it."
"Well," my mother counseled tenderly, "better give him
all the pieces. God can't fix your broken heart if you don't
give all the pieces to him." I'll always remember those
beautiful words: "God can't fix a broken heart if you don't
give him all the pieces." It's a great reminder that in
painful times, we don't have to go it alone.

—Jennifer Leigh Youngs, *Taste Berries for Teens*

Have you ever had to "pick up the pieces"?

?
_____
_____
_____
_____

The unspoken thoughts of even the
most private heart can be seen.

—ISUMI

Taste-Berry Actions: Turning to Others for Comfort and Support

Learning how to cope effectively with tough issues can help you grow stronger and wiser—and that's really important. But sometimes the challenges are simply too big for you to handle alone. Asking for help when you need it is a sign of strength. If you're facing struggles that seem overwhelming, rather than suffering alone or resorting to actions that are self-destructive, confide in people you trust. This is especially true if you are afraid of someone, feel depressed or suicidal, have an eating disorder, are pregnant or suspect you are, or are using drugs or alcohol. Don't feel you have to go these things alone. They are too much for even the strongest and most brave people. And besides, that's when people show their finest hour of being human. People want to help others. Allow those you trust to help you. Turn to an adult whom you feel you can trust to direct you to where you can get the help you need.

To whom, more than anyone else, can you best talk about tough stuff? What is it about this person that makes it "safe" for you to talk about what's in your heart?

 _____

_____

_____

In what ways does talking to someone about your heartache help you?

_____

_____

_____

_____

Who do you turn to for help when you're facing tough times? List three people whom you can lean on during hard times. How do they help you deal with tough issues?

Who: _____

How they help me cope: _____

_____

_____

Who: _____

How they help me cope: _____

_____

_____

Who: _____

How they help me cope: _____

_____

_____

*Keep knocking and the joy inside
will eventually open a window and
look out to see who's there.*

—RUMI

What does this quote mean to you?

_____

_____

_____

_____

What are the best words of advice or comfort anyone has ever given you? Who gave you the advice? How did it feel to you?

_____

_____

_____

_____

*A new moon teaches gradualness and deliberation
and how one gives birth to oneself slowly.*

—RUMI

Taste-Berry Actions: Comforting Others

When you see someone who is obviously heartbroken and needing comfort, what can you do to comfort that person? What do you think are the magical, soothing words and actions to help someone make it through the moment and perhaps help heal his or her wounded heart? Exactly what would you say and do? In what ways does this make you feel like a "taste berry"?

_____

_____

_____

_____

_____

_____

_____

_____

_____

*The fragrance always remains in
the hand that gives the rose.*

—HEDA BEJAR

About the Authors

Bettie B. Youngs, Ph.D., Ed.D., is a professional speaker and the internationally renowned author of sixteen books translated into twenty-nine languages. She is a former Teacher-of-the-Year, university professor and executive director of the Phoenix Foundation and president of Professional Development, Inc. She is a long-acknowledged expert on teens and has frequently appeared on *NBC Nightly News*, CNN, *Oprah* and *Geraldo*. *USA Today*, the *Washington Post*, *Redbook*, *McCalls*, *Working Woman*, *Family Circle*, *Parents Magazine*, *Better Homes & Gardens*, *Woman's Day* and the National Association for Secondary School Principals (NASSP) have all recognized her work. Her acclaimed books include *Taste Berries for Teens: Inspirational Short Stories and Encouragement on Life, Love, Friendship and Tough Issues; Safeguarding Your Teenager from the Dragons of Life; How to Develop Self-Esteem in Your Child; You and Self-Esteem: A Book for Young People; Taste-Berry Tales;* the Pulitzer-nominated *Gifts of the Heart;* and the award-winning *Values from the Heartland*. Dr. Youngs is the author of a number of videocassette programs for Sybervision and Nightingale/Conant and the coauthor of the nationally acclaimed *Parents on Board,* a video-based training program to help schools and parents work together to increase student achievement.

Jennifer Leigh Youngs, twenty-five, is a speaker and workshop presenter for teens and parents nationwide. She is the coauthor of *Taste Berries for Teens: Inspirational Short Stories and Encouragement on Life, Love, Friendship and Tough Issues* and author of *Health, Fitness & Beauty for Teens; A Stress-Management Guide for Teens,* and *Goal-Setting Skills for Young Adults.* Jennifer is a former Miss Teen California finalist and Rotary International Goodwill Ambassador and Exchange Scholar. She serves on a number of advisory boards for teens and is the International Youth Coordinator for Airline Ambassadors, an International organization affiliated with the United Nations that involves youth in programs to build cross-cultural friendships; escorts orphans to new homes and children to hospitals for medical care; and delivers humanitarian aid to those in need worldwide.

To contact Bettie B. Youngs or Jennifer Leigh Youngs, write to:

Youngs, Youngs & Associates

Box 2588

Del Mar, CA 92014